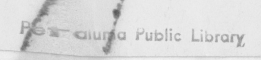

THE GOLDEN CARNATION
And Other Stories Told in Italy

The Golden Carnation

And Other Stories Told in Italy

by FRANCES TOOR

Illustrations by ANNE MARIE JAUSS

Lothrop, Lee & Shepard Company, Inc.

NEW YORK

Contents

FOREWORD

* * * * * * * * * *

* * * * * * * * * *

AIRY tales are usually compounded of earthy common sense and pure fancy. Italy's folk legends have both to a superlative degree: on the one hand, a sturdy sense of the commonplace, and on the other, the quality of unsurpassed imagination.

Many of these traditional folk tales mirror attitudes toward life which are as common today as when the tale was first told. Practical proverbs and pithy maxims are interwoven with adventure in the narratives. "Overcome difficulties by labor" says one character. "God helps those who help themselves," says another. "Tax collectors leave you only your eyes to weep with" is a third wry observation.

The Italian nature, for all its love of the beautiful, is also hard and practical, often to the point of cynicism. This is revealed in many Italian fairy tales in which the hero does not hesitate to violate his pledged word when he faces an unscrupulous foe. Nor does he hesitate to be ruthless and cruel when the circumstances call for it. So bad old witches are deceived, to their ultimate undoing, and the heads of evil monsters are cut off by the dozen, without tears or regrets.

In fairy tales of all lands, animals figure prominently.

Italian legends are no exception. Fishes, birds, mice, ants, as well as lions and eagles, behave and talk like men. If anything, they are a little more human in their conversation and behavior than are the legendary animals of other lands. Their gratitude is often displayed, and their help freely given, in such a way that one may wonder whether men or animals are the higher species.

Curses and spells, prophecies and soothsayings are another important ingredient in the conventional fairy tale. Italy's curses are perhaps a little more pointed, her prophecies a little more precise, than others. Yet even these threats may be circumvented. The mandril of one tale, who was supposed to make his appearance after seven years and claim the heroine, simply fails to appear when she marries the hero and thus the evil spell is blunted.

The Italians seem to make no real distinction between the fairy tale and the mythological legend, for Italian fairy tales go back to Roman and even pre-Roman times. Some of them have their foundation in the ancient Indo-European stock of folk tales, and appear barely changed from their Greek, Germanic or Celtic counterparts. Others, however, stem peculiarly from Italian soil.

Included in this collection, for instance, are typical fairy tales about heroes who go off on long journeys in search of a beloved lady, or who must perform a series of difficult labors, aided by benign animals, kindly gnomes or good fairies. There are also stories straight out of Greek mythology, like the legend of Alpheus and Arethusa, or that of Pluto and Persephone. There is a variation of the old legend, in the Roman tradition, of the founding of Rome. From the Dolomites comes the delicate story of how the edelweiss was brought to the earth from the moon. From Sicily comes the hardy tale of how the island was first named, as well as the medieval legend of King Frederick and his loyal retainer who gave his life to hold up forever the island in the blue-green Mediterranean. There is the combination of an older myth with more recent history in the tale of how King Roger snatched Sicily from the Saracens while rejecting the help and advantages of Fata Morgana (Morgan le Fay), the enchantress who figures largely in Arthurian legends. There is even an attempt to explain the uncanny mirages of the Strait of Messina, by which the distant city of Palermo becomes visible from the mainland of Italy.

Thus a volume of Italian and Sicilian fairy tales and legends acquires an anthropological and historical value, as well as providing high entertainment. In origin the fairy tale may not have been primarily devised for children, but for grown-ups whose love of the fictional, the adventurous, the fanciful, outstripped their pedestrian knowledge of the world around them, and led them to accept at face value the more un-believeable features of tales that may have had possible foundations in fact.

Even today, in parts of Italy and Sicily, the miraculous exploits of mythological and legendary heroes continue to be recounted by *cantastorie*, those often illiterate bards who wander from village to village singing the old songs of Roland and Charlemagne of France, of Roger and Frederick of Sicily, which in the bright setting of the Tyrrhenian and Ionian Seas, have lost neither their charm nor their power. Nor is it an accident that the gay designs to be found today on the brightly painted wine-carts of Sicily portray episodes from a partly historical, partly legendary past.

Who can say, after all, where truth ends and legend begins? Is not modern truth stranger than ancient fiction? In the light of hurtling jet planes, can we be certain that the flight of Daedalus and Icarus was merely a flight of the imagination? With sputniks and luniks circling in outer space, may not the charming tale of the Prince of the Dolomites and the Moon Princess be something more than a dream?

So let the reader of these lovely tales relax and enjoy them and remember that most of these stories were once listened to, in earnest, by young and old alike.

MARIO PEI

PART ONE

TALES OF
ENCHANTMENT

*   *   *

THE GOLDEN

CARNATION

* * * * * * * * * *

* * * * * * * * * *

NCE there was a merchant in Italy who had three daughters. Belinda was the youngest and the most beautiful and she was the one he loved the best. One day when he was setting out on a long voyage to India, he asked each of his daughters, "What would you like me to bring back for you?"

"For me a corset embroidered without a needle," the eldest replied.

"For me a dress all covered with tiny golden bells," said the second.

When Belinda's turn came, she said, "Anything that pleases you."

"But name something," insisted her father.

"Very well," said Belinda, "bring me a golden carnation."

The merchant reached his destination, attended to his business, and bought the presents for his two elder daughters. However, only when he was halfway home did he realize that he had forgotten the golden carnation he had promised Belinda.

While he was considering what to do, he saw before him a garden filled with every kind of plant. He entered and called,

15

'Gardener, where are you?" But no one answered. He began to walk about and, to his great surprise, came upon a plant which bore several golden carnations.

"What harm would there be in my picking one of those flowers?" he said out loud. "If the owner comes, I shall be glad to pay him any price for it." And he broke off one of the beautiful blossoms.

At that moment an ugly wizard appeared before him. "Who has given you permission to pick that flower?" he demanded.

"I took it because I love my daughter Belinda too much to disappoint her," and the merchant told him about her request.

"Well, then," said the wizard, "since you have picked the carnation, the only way you can pay for it is to bring your daughter here within three days. If you do not, your house will fall down around you in ruins."

With this the wizard disappeared and the merchant went on his way, sighing at every step. When he arrived at his house, he gave each of his daughters her gift, but tried not to let them see how worried he was.

His daughters, however, could see that something was worrying him, and finally the eldest one asked, "What is the matter with you, Father?"

"Oh, nothing," he replied. But they would not be put off, and finally he told them about the wizard's strange request and threat.

Afterward, when they were alone, the elder sister said, "It is all your fault, Belinda. Had you not asked for something so impossible, this would never have happened. Now we shall lose everything!"

So Belinda resolved to go to the wizard and begged her father to accompany her. The father, after much coaxing, consented with a heavy heart, and on the third day, he set out with his daughter for the wizard's palace.

There was no one in the garden when they arrived, but in the palace they found a table set with many delicious dishes, and since they were hungry, they sat down to enjoy the wizard's hospitality.

When they had finished their meal, the wizard appeared. The father's heart ached, for he was as ugly as Belinda was beautiful. "From today on," the wizard said to Belinda, "you are the mistress of this palace and garden." Then he disappeared.

Her father had returned home to his business, so Belinda was very lonely the first day. But on the second day at noon the wizard reappeared and shared the repast laid for her. To her surprise she found that he was very kind. After they had eaten, they went down together into the garden. As they strolled about, Belinda inquired the name of this plant and that and he explained everything patiently and amiably, mentioning its special virtue. One tree attracted her attention more than the others. "And this tree?" she asked.

"This," he answered, "is the tree of laughter and tears. When its leaves point skyward, it is a sign that there is happiness and laughter in your house, but when they point downward, there is weeping."

Belinda soon became accustomed to her new life and found that she was no longer lonely. She enjoyed picking the flowers in the garden and feeding the gaily-colored birds.

One day as she and the wizard were walking past the tree of laughter and tears, she noticed the branches tilted upward more than usual. "What does it mean?" she asked the wizard.

He told her it was because her eldest sister was to be married and she asked his permission to attend the wedding.

"Of course," said the wizard, "but on this condition: that you return within three days. Take this ring with you. You must look at it often. If the stone turns toward your palm, it means that I am in need of you."

Belinda promised to return within three days and assured him that she would watch the ring carefully to see if all were well. If necessary, she said, she would come back sooner.

As soon as her gown and wedding gift were ready, a golden carriage appeared at the door and bore her away. The distance was long, but in her enchanted carriage she arrived in a few moments. She received a fond welcome and was happy to be reunited with her family. But she did not forget her promise to the wizard and returned promptly within the three days.

When her second sister was married she went home again to attend the wedding. This time she forgot to look at the ring as often as she should have. In fact, she forgot all about it until the third day when she found it turned inward. When she hurried back to the palace, the wizard, looking very pale, was waiting for her. He was plainly agitated and said gravely, "You must not let this happen again. Always watch the ring. If you don't, woe to us both."

After this, their daily routine went on undisturbed for some time. Then, one day on one of her usual visits to the tree of laughter and tears, she found all the branches pointing downward.

"What can be happening at my house," Belinda asked the wizard anxiously.

"Your father is very ill," he answered gently. "He may be dying."

"Oh, please let me see him once more," she pleaded.

"Yes, you may go, but remember to watch the ring and to return within three days," he said.

Her father was so happy to see his youngest and most beautiful daughter again that he began to recover. Belinda was so relieved that she forgot to look at the ring. In fact, she had taken it off one day to wash her hands and left it on a little table for three whole days. When she remembered to put it on again, she noticed the stone turning immediately toward the palm of her hand. Bidding her father farewell, she set out at once to return to the palace.

When she arrived, she found the wizard limp and barely breathing on the ground. Belinda, stricken with remorse, knelt at his side, and through her tears, said, "My dear friend, what is the matter? I'm so sorry I forgot to watch the ring, but I was concerned about my father. Otherwise, I would have been back within the three days."

The wizard hoarsely stammered some words in reply, and Belinda impulsively bent down and kissed him.

As soon as Belinda's lips touched his, the wizard rose swiftly to his feet. Then, to her astonishment, she saw before her a handsome young man.

"I am the king's son," he said. "A wicked witch enclosed me in an ugly body and my spell could not be broken except by a kiss of love. I have loved you from the moment I first saw you, and I would be proud if you would be my bride."

The king was delighted to have his son wed the lovely Belinda, and the wedding was celebrated with great rejoicing.

Belinda's father and her two sisters were invited to the wedding feast, but because the sisters begrudged Belinda her good fortune, they were turned into two carved marble columns. They still stand at the entrance of the palace where Belinda and the young prince lived happily together ever after.

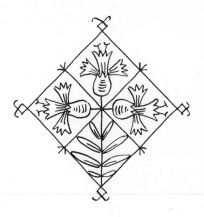

THE

FROG BRIDE

* * * * * * * * * *

* * * * * * * * * *

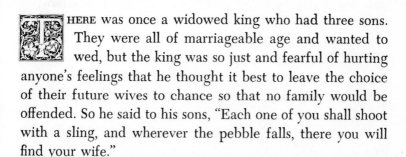

HERE was once a widowed king who had three sons. They were all of marriageable age and wanted to wed, but the king was so just and fearful of hurting anyone's feelings that he thought it best to leave the choice of their future wives to chance so that no family would be offended. So he said to his sons, "Each one of you shall shoot with a sling, and wherever the pebble falls, there you will find your wife."

The eldest son hit the house of a baker, the second one that of a weaver, but the stone shot from the sling of the youngest son fell into a pond where only a frog lived. The first two sons were fortunate, for the baker and the weaver each had a pretty daughter. The youngest son, however, did not fare so well, for he found himself betrothed to a green frog.

The two elder brothers were impatient to wed at once, but the king announced that they must all wait six months. The youngest son felt only relief at the delay.

The king decided to test the quality of each future princess. One morning he sent three pounds of flax to each, including the frog, and asked to have it woven into cloth. The one whose work was judged best, he announced, would be invited to live in the palace and manage the king's household.

A week later the king asked to see the cloth woven by each of his son's fiancées. The weaver's daughter displayed a fine piece of linen and the baker's daughter had done well, too. The king was pleased with the work of both. Then he looked at what the frog had sent and was a little surprised to find it rolled up in a walnut shell. But when he opened the walnut and began pulling out the cloth he exclaimed with delight. It was spun so fine that it looked like a spider's web. The king pulled and pulled and the cloth kept unfolding and unfolding, as though it would envelop the house. Finally the king said, "But this cloth has no end!" No sooner were the words out of his mouth than the cloth stopped unfolding and and rolled itself back into the walnut.

But still he deferred his decision. Next the king sent a gift of a puppy to each bride, saying, "She who rears it best shall come to live in the palace."

When the dogs were returned, the one which was raised by the baker's daughter, where there was always plenty of bread, was as round and plump as a wine cask. The one the weaver's daughter had reared looked in better condition; but neither dog had been taught any pleasing tricks.

Then the frog sent hers in a charming lacquered box. When it was opened, out jumped a beautiful little dog which frisked about and kissed the king's hand. It soon became the king's constant companion.

When the six months had passed the king said to his sons, "You may wed in a week and a day, and the frog shall henceforth be mistress of the palace."

The youngest son went to the pond to tell his fiancée that the king had at last set a date for the wedding.

"Who is there?" she asked, before she came up from the watery depths.

"One who loves you little," answered the prince.

"If he loves me little now," said the frog, "he will love me more later."

On the day of the wedding the two elder brothers rode with their brides-to-be in fine carriages. The resourceful frog fashioned one for her bridegroom out of a fig leaf which was drawn by two gray cats and two white mice who soon out-raced the horses of the others. Just as they drew up to the church the fig leaf was changed into a golden coach and the cats and mice into four fiery steeds. The frog's green skin disappeared and she was transformed into a beautiful young girl with eyes only for her beloved.

The prince, who had kept his word to wed his bride chosen with a sling, lived happily in the palace ever after with his frog bride, whom he did indeed grow to love more and more.

ZEZOLLA AND
THE DATE-PALM TREE

*   *   *   *   *   *   *   *   *   *

*   *   *   *   *   *   *   *   *   *

NCE upon a time there was a gentle girl named Zezolla, who was the only child of a rich prince, a widower, who did everything in his power to please her. Her governess, Carmonsina, taught her fine sewing and embroidery and lavished affection and sweet words upon her. All went well until one day Zezolla's father decided to marry the governess.

While the elaborate wedding celebrations were taking place, Zezolla was standing alone on a balcony of the palace when a little dove flew down to her and said, "If ever you need anything, send your request to the fairies on the Island of Sardinia, and they will grant your wish."

For a short time after the wedding, her new stepmother treated Zezolla as affectionately as ever, giving her the best of food and the finest of clothes to wear. But soon Carmonsina began to forget her sweet words. She brought forward her own six daughters, whom she had kept hidden until then, and so cajoled the prince that he took them to his heart and began to neglect his own daughter. One day Carmonsina sent Zezolla down to the kitchen to clean and scrub, and as

31

she was always to be found near the cindery hearth, she became known as "Cinderella the Cat."

She bore her new name with dignity, however, but wondered if she would ever be the Princess Zezolla again.

One day the king sent Zezolla's father on a special mission
to Sardinia. Before leaving he asked each one of his stepdaughters what she wanted him to bring back. One asked
for an elegant brocade gown, another for an ivory chess set,
another for a silver jar, another for a plumed headdress, and
so on. At last, and almost in mockery, he asked Zezolla, "And
what shall I bring for you?"

"Nothing," she answered, "except to take my greeting to
the fairies of Sardinia and tell them I beg them to send me
a token."

The prince went to Sardinia, transacted his business there
as quickly as possible, bought the presents for his stepdaughters, then returned to the ship without giving a thought
to Zezolla's request. The captain ordered the sails unfurled
and gave orders to start, but the ship would not move. They
tried every means, but they could not even get her out of the
harbor. Then the captain, worn out from his efforts, fell
asleep. In his dream a fairy appeared to him and said, "Do
you know why you cannot make your ship sail? It is because
the prince has broken his promise to his daughter. He remembered what his stepdaughters asked for, but forgot his
own flesh and blood."

As soon as the captain awoke, he went to tell his dream to
the prince, who felt ashamed that he had neglected his own
child. He went immediately to the grotto of the fairies and,
delivering his daughter's message, begged that they send her
some token. As he spoke, a beautiful fairy came out of the

grotto. She asked him to take Zezolla a date-palm plant, a golden spade, a golden can and a silken napkin. She was to plant the tree, using the the spade, to water it from the golden can and dry it with the napkin. He thanked the fairy and hurried back to the ship. The captain was then able to set sail and they returned home without any further trouble.

Each stepdaughter exclaimed over her present, and Zezolla was beside herself with joy over her little tree. She planted it at once and gave it such loving care that within a few days it grew as tall as a woman.

Then out of it popped a fairy, who asked Zezolla what she wanted most. "I would like to be able to leave the house in a fine dress without my family knowing it," she answered.

The fairy told her her wish would be granted if she would recite this verse:

> "My dear date-palm tree,
> My golden spade has dug for thee,
> My golden can has watered thee,
> My silken napkin has dried thee,
> Grant my fervent wish to me
> And give me thy finery."

If she wanted her own ragged garments again, the fairy said she should change the last lines to:

> Grant my fervent wish to me
> And take back thy finery.

Shortly afterward a festival was held which was to last for several days, and as was the custom, everyone promenaded in his best. While many strolled about on foot, the king and the nobles rode through the square in beautiful carriages, drawn by many horses.

The first day, all the members of the household—father, stepmother and sisters—went out, leaving Zezolla alone at the hearth. But she did not stay there long. She went quickly to the foot of her tree, recited the verse the fairy had taught her, and at once she was dressed like a princess. Outside, a fine carriage with four white horses awaited her, and she was attended by four smartly-dressed pages.

The king, who happened to be among the promenaders, was bewitched as soon as he laid eyes on the beautiful Zezolla. He instructed his most trusted attendant to follow her carriage and to find out for him who she was.

But Zezolla realized that her carriage was being followed and quickly threw out a bag of money that the tree had given her. The servant began to gather up the glittering coins, and she was able to enter the house unnoticed, in her own shabby gown.

The king angrily scolded his servant for having been diverted from his task by a few crowns and told him that he must not fail him after the next feast.

Meanwhile Zezolla had time to return her finery to the tree and when the family returned, they found her at her usual place at the hearth. To tease her, the girls described all that she had missed, making much of the mysterious lady who had captivated the king.

On the next feast day, after the family left the house, Zezolla went again to her date-palm tree to repeat the verse. Immediately the tree sent forth a number of maids, one with a comb, another with curling tongs, one with a box of rouge, another a flask of rose-water, others with a fine dress and jewels. They helped her dress and sent her off in a carriage drawn by six horses and attended by a footman and six pages.

The king had no eyes for anyone but Zezolla, who was admired by all the cavaliers and envied by all their ladies. "Who is she?" everyone wondered.

When she left, the king's attendant was once again ordered to pursue her, but this time she threw down a bag of jewels and pearls. The poor fellow could not resist the temptation to pick them up and so she had time to resume her place by the hearth before the family returned.

The frightened servant, having disappointed the king a second time, confessed his failure. The king was even more furious this time and shouted, "By the soul of your departed,

if you don't find out who that girl is the next time, I'll see to
it that you get a thorough beating."

On the last festival day, the same procedure was repeated.
As soon as the sisters closed the door behind them, Zezolla
ran to her tree and repeated the magic words. She was once
more magnificently dressed and placed in a golden coach,
and eight attendants in livery. Again the king was fascinated
and the ladies of the court, her stepsisters among them, were
more envious than ever.

On her way home, the same servant followed her and this
time kept close to the carriage. Fearing that she might be
overtaken, she cried to the horses, "Drive on!" The horses
started off at such a mad gallop that as the coach jolted, one
of her pretty shoes fell out.

The king's man was unable to catch up with her, but he
did retrieve her shoe and took it to the king, telling him
how the fair lady had eluded him once again.

The king would not give up his quest and he ordered his
heralds and trumpeters to proclaim that all the young women
in the land were to be invited to a banquet to be held at the
palace. They came by the hundreds, rich and poor, pretty
and ugly. After they had supped well of the best to be had,
with wine and entertainment, the king began trying on the
shoe. But it fitted no one.

The king was sadly disappointed, but he did not lose hope.
He invited his guests to return to another banquet the following evening. "Do not leave behind a single young
woman," he commanded, "whoever she may be."

Then the prince, Zezolla's father, spoke up, "Your Highness, I have a young daughter at home, but she is not fit to
take her place at the table with you."

"Bring her," replied the king, "for such is my wish."

When the guests returned to the banquet on the following day, Zezolla was with Carmonsina's daughters. At soon as the king saw her he felt in his heart that she was the one the shoe would fit and he could scarcely wait to try it on. After the banquet she was the first one he approached with the shoe and it flew out of his hand onto her foot.

The king then took Zezolla in his arms and led her to the canopy. There he put a crown on her head and ordered that from that moment on she would reign with him as his beloved queen.

THE WISE

WOODLAND MAID

* * * * * * * * * *

* * * * * * * * * *

HERE was once a hunter who lived with his wife, a son and a daughter deep in the forest. Once in a while the father went to the city to sell a few skins and to listen to the talk of the market-place, for his daughter Bianca always wished to hear of the world outside.

One day the king's son went hunting and lost his way in the forest. As dusk fell he wandered about, tired and famished, suddenly glimpsing far, far away a tiny glimmer of light. He followed it and reached at last the hut of the hunter, where he asked for a night's lodging and something to eat.

The hunter, who recognized the prince, said, "Your Highness, we have little to offer you, but we shall find something for you that we hope will leave you content."

The hunter asked his wife to prepare a fine roast capon for him. The prince called the family and gave the head to the father, the back to the mother, the legs to the boy and the wings to Bianca, reserving the rest for himself. After the meal the parents gave up their bed to the prince and went to sleep in the barn.

When Bianca thought the prince was asleep, she said

softly to her brother, "Do you know why the prince divided the capon among us in that manner?"

"Well, if you know, tell me," said the brother.

"He gave the head to Father," she said, "because he is the head of the family, the backbone to Mother because she has the whole household on her shoulders, the legs to you because you have to be nimble to run the errands that are entrusted to you, and the wings to me to fly to pick out a husband."

The prince, who was only pretending to be asleep, overheard their conversation. He thought the girl very intelligent, and as she was also pretty, he quickly fell in love.

The next day when he returned to his palace, he sent a servant with a purse of money for the hunter in return for his hospitality. Later he sent to Bianca a sweet pudding in the shape of a full moon, thirty tarts and a roasted capon, along with three questions that she was to answer. One was: "Is it full moon?" The second was: "Is it the thirtieth of the month in the woods?" and the third was: "Does the capon sing?"

The servant he sent, although usually trustworthy, was conquered by his gluttony and ate fifteen tarts, a good part of the sweet pudding and the capon.

Bianca understood that the questions referred to whether or not the messenger had delivered all that the prince sent, and she answered thus: "The moon is not full but only in the fifth tithe. It is only the fifteenth of the month in the woods, and the capon has gone to the mule." In the end she begged him to save the pheasant for the love of the partridge, which meant that he was not to punish the servant.

The prince understood her metaphor as well as she did

his, so he called his servant, shouting at him, "Rascal! You have eaten the capon, fifteen tarts and half of the sweet pudding. Be grateful to the girl that she has begged me not to punish you, as otherwise I would hang you!"

Some time later the hunter found a golden mortar and wanted to take it as a gift to the prince. But his daughter said to him, "You will be laughed at for this gift. You'll see that the prince will declare that the mortar is beautiful, but he will also say, 'Don't you know any better than to bring me a mortar without a pestle?'"

The hunter paid no attention to his daughter, but when he took the mortar to the prince he said exactly what she had foretold. So he said to the prince, "My daughter told me you would say those things to me. Ah, if only I had listened to her!"

The prince heard him and said, "Take these four ounces of flax to your daughter, who is so wise, and tell her to weave for me a hundred arm-lengths of cloth from it. If she does not, I shall have both of you hanged."

The poor hunter went home weeping, certain that he and his daughter would die, for who could weave a hundred arm-lengths of cloth from four ounces of flax!

Bianca came out to meet her father and asked why he was weeping. When she heard the reason, she said, "And for this you are crying? Here, give me the flax and leave the rest to me."

She extracted four tiny cords from the flax and said to her father, "Take these little cords to the prince and tell him when he will have made a loom for me from them, I shall weave for him a hundred arm-lengths of cloth from four ounces of flax."

When the father brought Bianca's message to the prince, he did not know what to say.

The next day the prince went to the forest to pay a visit to Bianca, and it happened that she was alone in the house. He knocked, but no one answered. He knocked even louder, but still there was no answer. The girl pretended to be deaf. Finally, the prince tired of waiting, pushed the door and entered. "Insolent one!" he said to her. "Who taught you not to open the door to a person of my station? And your mother and father, where are they?"

"Oh, who should have known it was you?" she said. "My father is where he needs to be and my mother is weeping for her sins. So you may leave, for I have other things to do besides entertain you."

The astonished prince went off in anger and complained to the hunter of his daughter's quick tongue, but found he could not forget her quick wit. He decided he must have her for his wife and sent a messenger to summon her to the palace as his intended bride.

The morning of their wedding feast was to bring still another test of her wisdom. As the wedding was held on a Sunday, many country people gathered in the market square. Two peasants, one with a handcart and the other with a burro, passed in front of the church, where the bells were calling the people to mass. The one with the cart let it stand outside and entered the church, while the other tied his burro to the cart and followed him in. While the services were going on the burro gave birth to a baby burro, and both the owner of the cart and the owner of the burro claimed it. As they could not come to an agreement they appealed to the prince to be the judge. The prince, who wished to get on with the wedding, hastily decided in favor of the owner of the cart. It was easier, he said, for the owner of the burro to tie his animal to the cart in order to claim the birth than for the cart to be tied to him. All the people were on the side of the owner of the burro, but the prince had spoken and there was no one to contradict him.

The poor man who was ordered to give up his baby burro sought the prince's bride, for, after all, she was one of the people. She advised him to throw his nets on the square just as the prince was about to pass, and indeed the prince, upon seeing the nets spread out, asked the man, "Are you crazy, trying to find fish on a square?"

And the peasant, who had been coached by the princess, answered him, "It is just as reasonable that I should find fish on this square as that a cart should give birth to a baby burro."

The prince then revoked his decision. But as he returned to the palace, where his bride waited, he thought about what the peasant had said and knew that no one but the wise woodland maid could have counseled him. He said angrily to his new wife, "Prepare to return to your home within an hour! Take with you the thing you care for most."

The princess remained calm and did not show any sign of fear or sadness. At dinner she poured the prince a glass of wine into which she had put a sleeping potion. And as soon as he had fallen asleep, she had him taken to her home in the forest.

It was a cold midwinter night, and through a hole in the roof snow began to fall on him. In the morning the cold flakes on his cheek awakened him and he called for his servants.

"What servants?" asked Bianca. "This is my house and here I command. Did you not tell me to take with me the thing I loved best? I have taken you because I love you above anything else. Now you are mine!"

The prince, bested once more, laughed heartily, they made peace and lived happily together ever after.

THE MELANCHOLY PRINCE

AND THE GIRL OF

MILK AND BLOOD

*   *   *   *   *   *   *   *   *   *

*   *   *   *   *   *   *   *   *   *

HERE was once a king who had a son who never smiled. He sat alone in his chamber and cared little for affairs of state nor anything under the sun.

One day his father, at his wits' end, was advised by one of his courtiers to set up three fountains on the square in front of the palace—one filled with wine, the second with oil and the third with vinegar—and to announce to the people that they could help themselves. The poor surged to the square in droves. They jostled and pushed, slipped and fell in the many rivulets and puddles. There was many a ridiculous scene as one after another lost his footing, but the prince, who looked on at the spectacle from the palace windows, never even smiled.

Finally, the fountains were almost exhausted when an old woman arrived with a little flask which she began to fill drop by drop with oil. This, strangely enough, amused the prince and when she had almost finished filling her flask, he idly flung a pebble in her direction. His aim was so good that it hit the bottle. It fell from her hands and broke into pieces. Then the prince threw back his head and, for the first time in his life, roared with laughter.

The old woman became very angry. She looked up at the prince and said, "So you are laughing at another's misfortune. Laugh all you want, but you will never know happiness until you find and win a girl of milk and blood."

Now the melancholy prince became exceedingly restless; he felt that the sooner he departed to look for a girl of milk and blood the sooner he would know happiness. So he took leave of his father and traveled through many different countries and cities but could not find a girl such as he sought anywhere.

One morning he found himself in the middle of a forest. It was hot and he became very thirsty, but nowhere could he find any stream or spring or any house where he might ask for a drink. He sat down under a tree to rest and he noticed three pomegranates hanging just above him. Would they not quench his thirst?

No sooner said that done. He picked one, opened it and out jumped a pretty maid, with a fair skin and rosy cheeks. "Ah," he thought, "here is my girl of milk and blood!"

The maid smiled at him, so he asked her, "Will you come to live with me?"

Instead of answering his question, she asked, "Have you anything to offer me?"

When he said he did not, she slipped back into the pomegranate and it became attached to the tree again.

He picked a second pomegranate and out jumped another lovely rosy-cheeked maid. They exchanged the same kind of questions and she also returned to the tree.

By this time he realized that he was making some mistake. So when he picked the third pomegranate and saw that the girl who emerged from it was even more beautiful than the other two, he answered he question by saying, "Yes, I will give you my heart if you will come back to my country with me."

She told him that her name was Marcella and that she was quite willing to go with him wherever he might take her. She and the other two maidens had been imprisoned in the pomegranates by an old witch, who, thinking them safely guarded, had gone, leaving in Marcella's care a magic wand, a hazelnut, a walnut and an almond.

Marcella and the prince soon found that the magic wand when waved in the air could summon a carriage with fast horses. Soon after they were whisked off in it, the old witch returned and called the girls out of the pomegranates. When only two appeared she immediately suspected something was amiss. "Where is Marcella?" she shrieked. "Where has she gone?"

The frightened girls could only say that Marcella had gone off with a young man in a carriage.

The witch immediately started off down the road in pursuit of the couple. When Marcella, who had expected that her absence would soon be noted, saw the old witch running toward them, she threw down the walnut and asked for protection in her flight. Immediately a roadside chapel appeared, of which she became the priest and the prince his assistant.

The old witch entered the chapel out of breath and asked the two if they had seen a young couple passing in a carriage. But the false priest pretended not to understand her and answered, "Did you say you wanted to hear mass? I shall begin in a moment, my good woman."

"No, I don't want to hear mass," shouted the witch in desperation. "I asked you if you saw a carriage with a young man and a beautiful young woman in it passing this way today."

"Ah, I see," said the disguised priest kindly. "All you want is a blessing. You shall have it."

The witch thought the pair either deaf or stupid. But since she could get nowhere with them she left, and the couple climbed back into their carriage and drove away.

Nothing daunted, the witch started down the road again, more determined than ever to catch Marcella and the young man. Being a witch, she could run fast even without any magic, so she was soon quite close on their heels. But Marcella saw her in time and threw down the hazelnut in her path. Suddenly a garden filled with beautiful roses appeared, and she and the prince became its caretakers.

The witch darted in the gate to ask for information about the fleeing couple. The gardeners answered, "Yes, you may pick any flowers you like, or if you prefer, we will gladly pick them for you."

The old witch shouted, "Who said anything about flowers? I only want to know if you saw a carriage passing this way," and she ran out upon the road once more.

The next time, as the old witch almost caught up to them, Marcella threw down the almond and a river came out of the ground. It looked like an ordinary stream, but its waters cut like steel knives. The witch hesitated only a moment and then threw herself in to swim across. But the waters sliced her to ribbons, and only then did Marcella and the prince feel they were truly safe.

They returned to free the girls in the pomegranates and all of them journeyed to the royal palace. The prince married his girl of milk and blood, the youngest and prettiest of the three, and arranged for the other two girls to wed two of his handsomest knights. And from that day forward the happy prince was never known again as the prince who never smiled.

THE

MAGIC MARE

* * * * * * * * * *

* * * * * * * * * *

HERE was once an old widow who had three sons. The first was called Giuseppe, the second, Nicola and the third, Franco. They were very poor, and as soon as the three were old enough to work they said to one another, "We must go out into the world to find a way of earning our bread."

One fine day, they took their few belongings and set off, leaving their old mother alone without anyone to help her. They went together as far as the nearest inn, shared a meal and then separated, each going his own way.

Each brother learned a different trade. Giuseppe became an expert thief, Nicola learned boiler-making and Franco, who was fond of day-dreaming, worked as a shepherd.

As soon as Franco finished his year's service he made ready to start home. He did not like to leave his widowed mother alone in her old age. As a parting gift his master gave him his wages and a black napkin from which, he assured him, he would be able to extract whatever money he needed.

He walked and walked until he came to the inn where he and his brothers had parted. About an hour later Nicola arrived and he and Franco greeted each other. Soon afterward another man arrived, but they did not recognize him as their brother Giuseppe. The next morning Giuseppe ordered a hearty breakfast prepared, for he was now quite rich, and suggested that they share it with him and that they all start out at the same time. His brothers did not understand the stranger's generosity, but when they stopped in the woods at noon to eat he told them that he was their brother Giuseppe and they embraced each other affectionately.

Upon arriving home, each went about his own business. Giuseppe played the gentleman and soon squandered his stolen money. Nicola continued to work hard at his boiler-making trade, while Franco helped his mother and drew forth coins from his magic napkin as he needed them. The mother, who was pleased to have all her sons at home again, showed a preference for her eldest, who seemed to her the richest.

Giuseppe's money, however, at last began to give out, while Franco still seemed to have plenty. Giuseppe became envious of Franco and devised a scheme by which he could ruin him. He knew that the king had heard of a beautiful young woman in a faraway land who wore seven veils and whom he wished to marry. But since no one knew just where she was, it was necessary for someone to find her. So the thief went to the king and said to him, "No one but my brother Franco can find the lady of the seven veils and bring her back to you."

The king immediately sent for Franco and commanded him to bring the lady of the seven veils to him if he did not want to lose his head. Franco did not know what to do, but he asked the king for three days in which to think of a plan.

With the coins from his magic purse Franco bought himself a pretty little mare, the Cavallina, who could talk as well as any person. As Franco returned to his home he went first to give the Cavallina her fodder. She noticed that her master had tears in his eyes, so she asked him why he was crying.

He told her what the king wanted of him and that he would surely lose his head. "Oh, no," she said. "Don't be afraid. Simply go back to the king and ask him for a golden bridle for me, a pound of bread crumbs and a leg of lamb. Then leave everything to me."

The king agreed to Franco's requests and he and his little mare rode off to the sea. There on the shore Franco saw a little fish flopping on the sand, trying to slip back into the waves. The Cavallina, who said to him, "Do help that poor little fish get back into the water. You never can tell when it might be of use to you."

Franco did as his little horse suggested and they rode away, leaving behind a grateful fish. Soon they came upon an army of hungry ants, and the Cavallina told Franco to scatter his bread crumbs and to give some of the leg of lamb to a famished crow. "It is always useful to make friends," the pretty little mare said wisely. Finally, they saw a dove being pursued by a snake, and Franco cut off the head of the snake to save the dove.

Then before they knew it they found themselves at the palace of the lady of the seven veils.

Before Franco entered it, the Cavallina said to him, "Listen carefully to what I have to say to you, if you wish to save your head. In this palace you will be greeted by seven young girls as beautiful as the sun. They will surround you and caress you. Then they will lead you into a fine salon and offer you lovely flowers, the most delicious fruit and valuable gems. You must refuse everything, no matter how tempting, and say, 'Better fruit, flowers and gems have I left at home.'

"The girls will then begin to sing and play various instruments, and each one will beg you to dance with her. But remember that if you accept a present or a kiss or dance with one of them, you will surely turn into marble. You must resist their charms. Finally, they will lead you onto a balcony to show you a fine view. That invitation you may accept. I shall be standing under that balcony, and you can leave the rest to me."

Franco did not miss a word of what the Cavallina had said and entered the palace well-prepared. But you can well imagine how he had to control himself not to yield to seven such beautiful girls. But he did allow himself to be led onto the balcony, underneath which his lovely little Cavallina was patiently waiting. The girls were enchanted by her and asked, "Whose pretty little horse is that with the golden bridle?" When he said it was his, they asked if they could mount her, and he said, "Of course."

The first one to try was the lady of the seven veils. As soon as she took hold of the reins, the Cavallina began to jump about, so she asked Franco if he would ride with her. He let her sit before him on the saddle and put his arm around her waist to steady her. Then the little mare picked up her heels and began to race so fast that not even an arrow could have caught up with her.

They soon arrived in a forest, where the lady let the wind carry one of her veils away. And as they raced along the seashore, she flung her ruby ring into the water.

At last they reached the king's palace. Franco took her in his arms and brought her to the king, saying, "Here, Your

Majesty, is the most beautiful girl in the world, who will be your wife."

Franco then thought that his troubles were over, but he was mistaken. The beautiful lady of the seven veils was not at all anxious to marry the king, so she kept finding excuses. She wanted the veil she had lost in the woods and the ruby ring she had cast into the sea returned to her before the wedding. So the king again ordered Franco to help him if he did not wish to lose his head. The Cavallina gave him courage and said, "Ask the king for more bread crumbs and meat, and don't worry."

Franco obtained the bread crumbs and the meat, mounted his good little mare and off they trotted.

As they came near the sea, they saw a little fish happily flicking its tail. "That is the same little fish whose life you saved by throwing it back into the sea," said the Cavallina. "Speak to it and ask it for help."

And Franco said to it, "Do you remember once when you were flapping about out of the water that I saved your life?"

"How can I forget it?" replied the little fish.

"Well, then, if you are grateful," said Franco, "now you can save mine in return. I must find the ruby ring of the lady of the seven veils, which she tossed into the sea when we passed by. If I don't, the king will cut off my head."

"Don't worry! Leave it to me," said the little fish, as it slid back into the water. In less than an hour it returned with the ring in its mouth and gave it to Franco. The little fish told him that a dolphin had found the ring but had carelessly left it in a conch shell from which the little fish had grabbed it and swum away with it. Franco thanked the little fish, and the Cavallina carried him off again.

Franco was happy over this stroke of good fortune, but there was still the veil to be found. In the woods, they came across the same hungry ants to whom he had once given breadcrumbs. They were still hungry so he gave them more crumbs. Then he met the crow whom he had fed. "Give it more meat," said the Cavallina, "and ask it to help you find the veil."

Franco gave the crow more meat and said to it, "Friend crow, this is the second time that I have saved you. Now will you do me a favor? A lady with whom I was riding threw off her veil here and the wind carried it away. Now the king has commanded me to find it. If I don't, he will have my head cut off. So I beg of you to help me."

"Don't worry, good youth!" said the crow. "I know where the veil is. A cuckoo has made her nest in it, but I shall go and bring it to you this instant."

The crow flew off and returned at once with the veil in its mouth. Franco expressed his thanks warmly, and the Cavallina bore him back to the king with the veil and the ring.

The king handed them over to the lady of the seven veils and said to her, "Now that you have what you wanted, when shall we be wed?"

"Not yet," she replied. "First you must take three heaps of cereals—one of corn, one of barley and one of oats—make one heap of them and within twenty-four hours separate them grain by grain into three heaps, as they were before they were mingled. If you cannot do that, I shall not marry you."

The king at once sent for Franco and commanded him to do it for him, with the usual threat of losing his head.

The poor youth ran to his Cavallina, and cried, "Oh, help me, help me! For this time I shall surely lose my head!"

"Don't be so frightened!" said the Cavallina soothingly. "Ask the king for more bread crumbs and we shall go."

The Cavallina trotted this time directly to the ants, and said to Franco, "Give those hungry ants more crumbs and they will do what you say."

Franco fed the ants and asked them to get into a sack, which they did. He took the sack to the heap of corn, barley and oats, emptied it, and in less than twenty-four hours the ants had separated them neatly into three heaps.

"Well, now shall we be married?" asked the king of the lady of the seven veils.

"No, not yet," she answered. "There is still something else you must do for me. I want a goblet of water from heaven and one from hell."

The king was becoming bad-tempered as a result of her

series of strange requests, but there was nothing he could do but call for Franco. And of course Franco always brought his troubles to his good and wise little Cavallina.

This time she took him to the dove he had saved from the serpent. "Dear little dove," he implored, "save me from death as I saved you from the snake."

"What is the matter?" asked the dove.

"I must return to the king with one goblet of water from heaven and one from hell," answered Franco. "If I don't, he will have my head cut off."

"My friend," said the dove, "I can bring you the goblet of water from heaven, but I am afraid to go to hell."

The dove's mate, which was hovering nearby, said, "I'm not afraid. I shall bring you the water from hell."

The two doves flew off together and after a while each returned with a goblet of clear water in its beak. Franco expressed his thanks to the pair and his little Cavallina trotted him back to the king. "Now," said the king to the lady of the seven veils, "you surely cannot ask for anything more, and we can be married at once."

"There is still one more thing I want," she said, "and it is the last."

"Well, what is it you want now?" asked the king in bad humor.

"I want Franco to be cut into pieces and put into a boiler," said the lady of the seven veils, as coolly as though she were asking for a glass of water.

The king thought it very cruel to treat Franco in this way, but he sent for him just the same and repeated to him the lady's wish, saying, "It must be done!"

Poor Franco began to tremble all over when he heard what

the king wanted of him. He asked for three hours' grace, which the king granted. And you can imagine to whom he ran to tell his newest, and worst of troubles.

The Cavallina comforted him and said, "Hurry! Mount me at once and we shall go racing around until I am all asweat. Then you will grease yourself with the drops from my flanks, and you need have no more fears."

Franco obeyed his good little horse. When he was well greased with her froth, he told the king he was ready.

Franco was cut into pieces and dropped into the boiler, which had been made by his poor brother Nicola. But he felt no pain at all. The lady of the seven veils then emptied the goblet of clear water from heaven into the boiler and Franco emerged all in one piece and the handsomest youth you ever saw.

Then the lady of the seven veils said to the king, "Why don't you also make yourself young and handsome before we wed? See how easy it is!"

The king was willing and asked Franco what he had done to protect himself from pain and to come out unscathed.

"I greased myself with the dregs from oil," replied Franco.

The king did the same, but it availed him little. He was cut into pieces and tossed into the boiler. When the lady of the seven veils added the goblet of water from hell, the flesh and bones of the unfortunate king went up in flames.

Then the lady of the seven veils turned to Franco and said, "You are the one who has suffered on my account, not the king. So, my dear Franco, you must marry me."

So he became king and could claim as his wife the most beautiful queen in the world. Being a king did not spoil his gentle nature, and he lived happily ever after with his queen and the good little Cavallina, who had saved his head by her wits.

Giuseppe was so jealous of his brother's good luck that he died from rage. But Franco took his boiler-maker brother Nicola and his mother to live the rest of their days in the palace.

THE YOUTH

WHO COULD BECOME AN ANT,

A LION OR AN EAGLE

* * * * * * * * * *

* * * * * * * * * *

NCE upon a time there was a poor fisherman who made only a bare living from the sea. One season the fish became even more scarce and he did not know what to do to make ends meet.

He cast his nets into the sea and pulled up a huge fish, which said to him, "If you will only let me go, I shall double your catch tomorrow."

The kind-hearted fisherman agreed and tried his luck the following day. This time his nets came up with more fish than he had ever caught before. But in a few weeks fish were scarce once more. One morning he caught the same big fish in his net. This time it said dolefully, "My time has now come. Cut me up into pieces and give one-half to the king, a piece to your wife, one to your mare and one to your dog. The smallest bone hang from a rafter of your kitchen. In years to come it will sweat blood if any of your sons is ever in danger."

The fisherman did as the fish had directed and distributed the pieces. Several months after eating the pieces of the fish his wife, his mare and his dog all gave birth to triplets the same day. One day some years later the eldest of his three sons said to his parents, "I want to see something of the world and make my fortune."

So Mario took leave of his family, asked his mother and father for their blessing and departed with a dog, a horse and some money.

After a journey of some hours, he came to a forest, where he saw a lion, an ant and an eagle standing near a dead burro. They wanted to divide it among themselves but could not agree as to which part should go to whom. When they saw Mario coming they hailed him and asked him to make the division. He was afraid at first that he might not please them but plucked up his courage and gave the flesh to the eagle, the brains to the ant and the bulk to the lion. They were all content with their share and Mario went his way.

He had gone but a few steps when they called him back and the lion said to him, "You have brought harmony among us, and we wish to compensate you for what you have done. When you need the strength of a lion, all you need to do to become one is to say, 'No more man, lion; the strength of a hundred lions.' When you wish to fly, say, 'No more man, eagle; the strength of a hundred eagles.'" "And when you need to be tiny to get yourself into tight places," put in the ant, "just say, 'No more man, ant; the strength of a hundred ants.'"

The youth thanked them all and went on his way. When Mario came to the sea he saw a dogfish out of the water, who said to him, "If at any time I can be of service to you, come to the sea and call, 'Dogfish, help me!'"

Continuing on his way he soon arrived in a city which he found all draped in black. "What has happened here?" he asked of a man, who replied, "We live in fear of a witch called the Nuvolaccia, or Storm Cloud, because she darkens our sky. Every year she demands as tribute from us a young girl, for she finds nourishment only in young girls' blood. If her demand is not met she will take revenge on our city. Now, alas, it is the turn of the king's own daughter!"

Mario asked if he could watch what was happening and he was told he was welcome to do so. Soon Mario heard drumming and saw a procession of soldiers followed by the king and queen, both weeping as they went. He followed them up a mountainside where he saw them prop the young princess, who had fainted, in a large golden chair and leave her alone to her sad fate.

After the procession had descended the mountain, Mario, who had remained hidden behind a clumb of bushes, saw the dread Nuvolaccia appear. She took the limp princess on her lap and began to prick drops of blood from one of her fingers. Then she put her in a carriage and drove off with her.

Mario quickly said, "No longer man, eagle; the strength of a hundred eagles." He immediately turned into an eagle and flew after the carriage, which soon turned in at the gates of a gloomy palace. The doors opened wide and the witch entered, carrying the princess. From his eagle's perch in a nearby tree Mario could see a room filled with frail young girls, all pale from loss of blood. They greeted the witch with cries of "Mamma, Mamma!"

She put the pretty princess on an empty bed and said to the girls, "Take care of her. I must leave you alone for a few days, as I must go on a journey."

Mario was near enough to hear her words, so as soon as she had gone he said, "No longer eagle, ant; the strength of a hundred ants."

He became an ant and was thus able to creep up to the girls' room without being seen. Then he became himself again. The girls were frightened at seeing a handsome youth appear suddenly among them, but they were too weak to protest. They soon saw that he was friendly, and one of them said to him, "Take care. We are imprisoned here by the Nuvolaccia. Should she return unexpectedly and find you, she will surely kill you."

"I am not afraid," he said. "I want to free you from her spell if I can." ,

Then Mario asked the princess, who had now regained consciousness, if she wished to send a token to her mother, for he was going to see her. She gave him an emerald ring, and in order not to lose another moment he became an eagle again. He flew quickly to the palace and, with the help of the princess's ring, secured an audience immediately with the queen. He told her that her daughter was safe but imprisoned, along with all the other young girls who had been sacrificed to the Nuvolaccia, and assured her that he would do all in his power to restore her to her parents. She promised to help him in any way she could.

When Mario returned to the witch's palace he brought with him nourishing food and medicine for the girls. He told them to say to the witch when she returned, "Dear mamma, while you were away we were talking and wondered what we should do if anything happened to you. How could we take care of ourselves if you were to die?" Mario added, "Perhaps she will reveal something to you that will help me destroy her forever."

When the witch returned, the girls showed her more affection than usual and asked her the questions Mario had suggested to them. "You must not worry about that, my pets," she answered, "for I shall never die."

"But," they asked, "how can you live forever?"

"You are all too weak," said the witch, "or I would take you to the topmost terrace to show you why I need not die like everyone else."

The girls assured her that they were indeed strong enough to accompany her. "If we may be certain that we will not be left alone in the world, we shall be happier," they pleaded.

"All right," she said, flattered by their interest. "We shall do it tomorrow."

The next day the witch led them to a staircase in the palace, which they bravely climbed in their exhausted condition. At the end of it was a terrace from which the witch pointed to the east, "See that mountain over there, far, far away? On the top of it lives a tiger with seven heads. For me to die it is necessary that a lion fight with the tiger and cut off his seven heads. Then someone must cut the tiger open and take out an egg from its body. Then he must hit me with it in the center of my forehead. Only then will I die. But if the egg is not afterward put into my hand, I shall have my revenge. Now do you see how impossible it is that I should die like ordinary mortals?"

"It is certain that our mamma will never die and leave us," said the terrified girls in chorus. They went back to their beds, and as soon as the witch left them alone again Mario appeared among them. They then related to him all she had said.

Mario promised them that he would see what could be done. He then turned himself into a fierce lion and went forth to fight the seven-headed tiger on the mountain-top.

In the meantime the Nuvolaccia confessed to the girls, "I cannot imagine what is the matter," she said. "I have never felt so weak in my life." All week she seemed to lose strength day by day. At the same time Mario, as a lion, was fighting the tiger valiantly, but he was able to take off only one head a day.

Finally, after finishing off the last of the seven heads, he changed back into a man, cut open the tiger's body and found the egg. But although he carried the egg very carefully on his way back to the witch's palace, he somehow dropped it into the sea. He then remembered what the dogfish had told him and called for help. When the dogfish answered his call, he asked, "Have you found a tiger's egg in the water? If you have, please give it to me at once."

The dogfish said he had swallowed the egg to keep it safely for him. Mario thanked him, took the egg and arrived with it at the witch's palace. When the handsome youth stood before her with the tiger's egg in his hand the Nuvolaccia could hardly believe her eyes, but she did not want to let him know that it meant anything to her. She only remarked, "What an unusual egg you have! Will you not give it to me?"

"Yes, I have come halfway around the world and across the sea to bring it to you, for I have heard of your powers," said Mario, "but in return I would like to see the beautiful girls who live with you restored to their former selves. Surely that is not a difficult task for you to perform."

The Nuvolaccia was so eager to obtain the egg that she quickly touched each girl's cheek with a magic wand and then held out her hand greedily. But Mario kept the egg out of her reach and added, "Not until you have provided a coach and four horses for each one."

In a trice the courtyard was full of prancing horses and golden coaches, and in the confusion Mario flung the egg at the witch. It hit her in the center of the forehead and she fell dead at his feet. After Mario had assisted the now rosy-cheeked girls into the carriages, he remembered to put the egg in the witch's hand before he joined the happy princess. But in his haste to depart he did not notice that the fateful egg had rolled out of the witch's hand.

The king and queen wept with joy over the return of their daughter and gladly gave her hand in marriage to Mario.

The entire kingdom rejoiced at being freed from the threat of the Nuvolaccia, and Mario spent many happy days with his princess.

But one morning Mario noticed a strange dark mist which seemed to be descending to the earth. "Come and look at that storm cloud," he said to his wife. "I have never seen anything like it. I would like to get a closer look at it." She begged him to stay, but he put on his hunting clothes, called for his dog, mounted his horse and rode toward it.

When he reached the mist at last he passed through it to find a hill crowned with a castle. Two beautiful women in black and silver robes came forward to meet him and invited him to visit it. He accepted their invitation and they brought him into a pleasant room and asked him if he would not play a game of chess with them.

"With pleasure," he replied, and lost the game good-naturedly. Afterward they asked if he would like to see their garden. As they walked through it Mario noticed many natural-looking marble statues, and before he realized what was happening, he, his horse and his dog were also turned into marble. The two beautiful sorceresses who had lured him to their castle were sisters of the Nuvolaccia and were determined to avenge her death threefold.

Meanwhile the princess waited alone in the palace for her dear Mario to return. In his father's cottage the kitchen was flooded the next morning with blood from the little bone of the talking fish, so his family knew at once that Mario was in grave danger. So the second brother of the triplets took one of the three horses and dogs who had been born at the same time and set out to look for him.

He passed by Mario's palace, and the princess happened

to be standing at the window. As he very much resembled Mario she thought it was he and called to him. From the way she talked he understood that it concerned Mario and that she had mistaken him for his brother, so out of sympathy for her he decided to act as if he were Mario. The next day he also found himself strangely drawn toward the faraway mist and went off with his horse and dog. But, like Mario, he soon joined the petrified statues in the garden.

In the meantime the princess waited sadly for Mario's return, and in the kitchen of the fisherman's family the bone again dripped blood. Then Mario's third brother took the third horse and third dog and set out to look for his two brothers. When he arrived at the palace the princess beckoned to him, called him in and received him as though he were her husband, but with reproaches instead of caresses. She felt she had been badly treated, while he did not know what it was all about. The bewildered young man stayed overnight, but the next day he, too, was drawn toward the mist.

Passing through the mist, the third brother met an old man, who asked him where he was going. "I am looking for my two brothers," he replied, "whom I feel certain are in danger."

"Yes," said the old man, "your brothers are under the spell of the Nuvolaccia's sisters and are now marble statues. You will soon meet them disguised as beautiful young women. They will invite you to play a game of chess with them in their palace. You may accept their invitation, but tell them you cannot play without these two pawns. Before starting the game, say that if you win they must do whatever you ask and that if they win you will put yourself at their mercy. As they will feel sure of winning, they will agree. However, these magic pawns will insure your victory. Then you must insist that they bring all of the marble statues in their garden back to life. After that you can do with them whatever you wish."

He thanked the old man and went on. The two beautiful witches of the castle on the hill extended the same invitation to him as they had to his two brothers. He accepted their invitation, but to their great surprise he won the chess game. The witches knew at once that their magic power was threatened and begged him to spare their lives.

He told them that first they would have to return to life all the men and animals that they had petrified. They took

their magic wands and went quickly about, touching the statues with them until all of them became living, breathing creatures once more. Then, before the young man had time to think what to do next, the dogs fell upon the witches and tore them to pieces.

Thus the three sons of the fisherman were happily reunited and all returned to the palace. The poor princess was so confused when she saw the three youths together that at first she could not tell which one was her husband, but Mario took her into his arms and introduced his brothers. They vowed never to be parted again, the fisherman and his wife were sent for and all lived happily in the palace.

A KISS FROM

THE BEAUTIFUL FIORITA

* * * * * * * * * *

* * * * * * * * * *

NCE a king had four children, three daughters and one son, who was heir to the throne. One day the king remarked to the prince, "My son, I have decided to marry your sisters to the first three men who pass the palace today exactly at noon."

It so happened that the first man to pass that day was a keeper of pigs, the second a hunter and the third a gravedigger. The king summoned the three men to the palace, spoke with each of them and announced to the pig-keeper that he was to marry the eldest princess, the hunter that he was to marry the second and the gravedigger the third.

The astonished men thought they must be dreaming but, seeing that the king was in earnest, they thanked him and departed in great confusion murmuring, "As you wish, Your Majesty."

Although his son begged his father not to insist that his sisters wed men of such lowly occupations the king paid no attention and went ahead with his plans. The prince refused to attend the triple wedding ceremony but instead went alone to the garden.

As he mused there among the flowers he heard a voice

which seemed to come from a white cloud say, "Proud prince, you will never be happy again until you obtain a kiss from the lips of the beautiful Fiorita, who is more beautiful than any flower you have ever seen."

Lost in thought, the prince pondered at the words he had heard, finally shook himself awake, as from a nightmare, and said, "I can no longer be happy under my father's roof, since my sisters will no longer be here. Therefore I may as well wander through the world until I obtain a kiss from the beautiful Fiorita, whoever she may be."

Without further ado and without bidding his father or sisters farewell, he set off over mountains and plains, without finding anyone who could tell him where the beautiful Fiorita might be.

One day he emerged from a forest into a beautiful valley in the midst of which stood a comfortable manor house. As he approached the well in the courtyard to take a drink of water a youngster playing near it began to cry. A young woman came running out to see what had alarmed the child and, upon seeing the prince, threw her arms around his neck, saying "Welcome, welcome, dear brother!"

It took the prince some time to realize that she was indeed his eldest sister. She took him to her husband, who had prospered and now owned several rich farms. The prince asked how his other two sisters and their husbands had fared.

"We are all well and happy," his brother-in-law replied. "One day's journey toward the east will bring you to your second sister and two more in the same direction to your third sister."

"But I cannot tarry to see them, for I cannot rest until I find the beautiful Fiorita," said the prince. "I don't know where she is, whether where the sun rises or where it sets."

"You are twice fortunate. You will see your most beloved youngest sister and at the same time you will learn where you may find the beautiful Fiorita," said his kind brother-in-law. "But before you leave I want to give you something to remember me by. Since I was formerly a pig-keeper, I shall give you three magical pigs' hairs. If you are in danger and pigs can be of any use to you, throw down these hairs and the pigs will appear to help you out."

The prince gratefully accepted the present of the hairs and, taking affectionate leave of them, quickly resumed his journey.

Upon arriving at his second sister's home, the prince received no less cordial a welcome. He was anxious to hurry on, so he did not stay long. At parting, his second brother-in-law, the hunter, also offered him a gift—a bunch of birds' feathers—saying, "If ever you need the help of birds, just throw down these feathers onto the ground and they will come flying to your aid."

At the end of the third day, the prince reached the home of his favorite youngest sister, and their reunion was filled with great tenderness. He was also heartily welcomed by her husband. The prince told his sister of his eagerness to find the beautiful Fiorita, and she gave him a letter to an elderly woman who could give him any information he needed. His third brother-in-law also gave him a parting gift. As he had been a gravedigger, his present took the form of a tiny bone of a baby's foot. "If a baby can be of any use to you when you are in trouble," he said, "throw this bone onto the floor."

Finally the prince arrived in the country of the beautiful Fiorita, whose father was its king. He found that the house of the old woman his sister had told him to see was located directly opposite the palace, so that she could tell him at which window the beautiful Fiorita was likely to appear every morning at dawn.

The next morning, as the prince watched eagerly, the princess came to the palace window covered only with a sheer white veil. He was so moved at the sight of her beauty that he would have fallen had not the old woman caught him.

She tried to persuade him to give up any idea of winning the beautiful Fiorita. "The king does not want to give his daughter in marriage to any man," she said, "so he puts every possible obstacle in her suitors' way. If they fail they must die, and many a prince has already lost his life for love of her."

"But having seen her," he sighed, "I must have the beautiful Fiorita as my bride even if I should die in the attempt."

Having also learned from the old woman that the king sought to obtain all sorts of rare musical instruments for his daughter, who loved music, the prince went to a harpsichord-maker and said to him, "I would like you to make a harpsichord for me which will play three sonatas, each of which will last a day or a night. It must be large enough so that a man can hide inside it. If you can make such an instrument for me I will pay you a thousand ducats. When it is finished I shall get into it and you will then take it to the palace to play for the king. If he wants it, you may sell it to him with the provision that you must remove the instrument to your workshop every three days in order to retune it."

The harpsichord-maker agreed to fulfill his part of the bargain, and the king proved to be delighted with the instrument and readily agreed to the special conditions. It was moved into his daughter's bedroom by the king, who said to her, "My dear child, I do not want you to lack amusement day or night. This will provide continual music for you."

Her maids-in-waiting were accustomed to sleep in a room adjoining the bedroom of the beautiful Fiorita. The first night, after making sure that they were all fast asleep, the prince crept out of the harpsichord and called softly, "Beautiful Fiorita, my beautiful Fiorita!"

She awoke in terror and called, "Maids, come quickly. There is someone in my room calling my name."

The maids came hurrying in but found no one, as the prince quickly re-entered the instrument. The same thing happened once again, and still the maids found no one. So the princess said to them, "I am sorry to disturb you. It must be my imagination. So if I call you again, do not come. That is my order."

The prince, watching everything from his hiding place, heard what she said. Then, as soon as everyone was asleep again, the prince approached her bed and whispered, "Beautiful Fiorita, I beg for the favor of a kiss from your lips. If you do not grant it, I shall die."

This time she was even more frightened and called her maids in a trembling voice but, obeying her command, they did not come. Then, looking at the handsome prince, she regained her calm and said simply, "You have won."

She kissed him on the lips and gave him a beautiful rose. "Take this rose," she said, "and wear it over your heart. It will bring you good luck."

The prince accepted it and did as she bade him. Then he told the beautiful Fiorita he was determined to take her back to his father's kingdom as his bride.

The beautiful Fiorita, who preferred the youth to all her previous suitors, told him she would gladly marry him but warned that it would be necessary for him to surmount any obstacles which her father might put in his way. "First," she said, "he will send you to a certain hidden chamber in which you must pick me out from among a hundred veiled maidens. But you need not worry, for the rose you have taken from me will lead you to me like a magnet. For the rest, you will be on your own. I shall pray for your success."

The prince asked for an audience with the king the very next day. He received the youth with all due courtesy but told him that the betrothal could take place only if all the tests were met.

With the help of the rose the prince easily passed the first test. "Well done," said the king, when the prince recognized the beautiful Fiorita from among the hundred veiled maidens. "But that is not all. Now you shall be locked in a large room full of fruit all of which you must eat in one day—at the price of your head."

Fortunately the prince recalled the three pigs' hairs and his brother-in-law's advice. So he took out the pigs' hairs from his pocket and threw them down on the floor. Almost immediately a large herd of pigs appeared, ate up all the fruit and disappeared. So he triumphed again.

But the king immediately proposed still another test. This time the prince was commanded to put the beautiful Fiorita to sleep with the song of wild birds of the air. The prince then recalled the bunch of feathers his hunter brother-in-law had given him and threw them down on the floor. At once a flock of beautiful birds flew into the room, singing so divinely that not Fiorita but the king himself fell fast asleep.

But as soon as he awakened he said to the prince, "Tomorrow morning you must show me a two-year-old baby who will be able to speak and call you by name."

The prince said to the beautiful Florita whom he had married secretly while the king was asleep, "Let us have one night's happiness at least, and perhaps before morning some good saint may come to our assistance, even though your father thinks he already has my head."

Remembering his eldest sister's little boy whom he had first seen playing at the well, the prince took the little bone his gravedigger brother-in-law had given him and threw it on the floor as soon as the morning light flooded their room. When the king entered a little baby boy ran to meet him

89

and wanted to place a golden apple on his crown. Then he returned to the bed and called, "Father, Mother!" The king kissed the baby, blessed the couple and, taking off his crown, put it on the head of his son-in-law, saying, "You have won it gloriously. It is now yours."

After this the king made public announcement of his daughter's wedding and there was great rejoicing throughout the land for several days. The prince's sisters, with their husbands, attended the festivities and his father came also when he heard the good news. He was so happy to see his son whom he thought he had lost forever that he put his own crown on his head.

Thus the prince and the beautiful Fiorita became king and queen of two kingdoms, over which they reigned happily until the end of their days.

IRON, STEEL

AND STRONGEST-OF-ALL

*   *   *   *   *   *   *   *   *   *

*   *   *   *   *   *   *   *   *   *

NCE upon a time an old peasant who felt he had come to the end of his days called his son and daughter, Pietro and Maria, to his bedside and said, "My dear children, all I have to leave you is this small plot of land, the hut we live in and three sheep. But I shall die content if I know you will promise to share everything as a loving brother and sister should." They promised to do as he wished, and he died in peace.

For a while all went well with the brother and sister. Every day when Pietro had finished his chores on the little farm he would take their three sheep to pasture on a pretty green meadow nearby.

One day a gentleman passed by with a fine dog. The young peasant greeted him courteously and could not help exclaiming, "What a beautiful dog you have!"

The man replied, "It is a very fine dog. Perhaps you would like to buy it."

"I have no money," said the youth.

"That makes no difference," answered the man kindly. "If you will trade me one of your sheep, I shall give you the dog in exchange."

Pietro gladly agreed to the bargain and asked what the dog's name was.

"His name is Iron," said the man, as he led the sheep away.

When Pietro showed the beautiful dog to his sister, she was not at all pleased. "It is only a useless bread-eater!" she complained.

The following day the young peasant went to the pasture again with his two sheep and the dog. At about the same time as on the previous day another gentleman passed by with another dog whom Pietro thought was even finer than the first.

"If you would like to have another beautiful dog," said the stranger, "I shall give this one to you in exchange for one of your sheep."

Pietro hesitated for a moment, fearing his sister's anger, but yielded to his strong desire to possess the other dog. He made the exchange and asked the dog's name. "Steel," answered the man and disappeared.

When Maria saw a second dog and only one sheep left, she cried in despair, "And now what shall we do without wool for our winter stockings and shirts?"

The next day Pietro went to the pasture with his two dogs and the one remaining sheep. At the same hour a third gentleman passed with a third and still more beautiful dog. Pietro could not help exclaiming over its beauty, and the man offered it in exchange for the last sheep. And when he asked for the name of this dog, he was told it was "Strongest-of-all."

When he came home this time with three dogs and his last sheep gone, his sister was even more furious. Pietro tried to calm her and said patiently, "Don't worry about what our father left us. For my part, I am content with the dogs I received and a bag of bread. I shall go to seek my fortune and leave you the rest." The spiteful Maria stayed up all night to bake the bread that her brother might leave the sooner.

The next morning the poor youth took his bag of bread but did not know which way to go. But he trusted in God and called joyously, "Iron, Steel and Strongest-of-all, let's go!"

Upon hearing the order, the three dogs jumped forth with great glee, and Pietro followed them toward the rising sun with his bag of bread upon his back.

They walked and walked when suddenly the dogs plunged into a forest as though they knew their way, but all of them were soon drenched by a thunderstorm. Pietro despaired of finding shelter for the night, but his dogs led him up to a fine palace the doors of which opened silently to let all four of them in.

There was no one to receive them, but they found a roaring fire and a table set with all sorts of good things to eat. As hunger asks no questions, Pietro sat down and ate heartily, even before standing before the fire to dry his wet clothes. When night came the house was suddenly illuminated with many candles. Again a fine meal was set upon the table to which the youth and his dogs did full justice.

After a while Pietro began to feel sleepy, and his dogs pulled him gently into a bedroom. He undressed and went to sleep, with one dog at the foot of his bed and one on each side, and felt well-protected, as they formed a cross.

In the morning the dogs greeted Pietro affectionately. They had already become very fond of their master and he of them. They went down all together to the dining hall and found the table set with a savory breakfast. Afterward, Pietro noticed a fine gun in a corner, which made him decide to try his luck at hunting in the woods. The dogs jumped up eagerly as he called them and they all went out together.

When it was nearly noon, the dogs led their master back to the palace, where they found a delicious meal prepared for them. Still, no one was in sight anywhere. Pietro was mystified, but he ate hungrily just the same and went out again with his dogs in the afternoon. Before dark the dogs again led their master home. Supper was served by invisible servants and, after a day of exercise outdoors, they all slept soundly.

This pleasant routine continued day after day and might have done so indefinitely if it were not that Pietro was too good-hearted to forget his sister. "I'm living here like a lord," he thought, "while my poor sister is probably in need. By rights should she not be sharing this good life with me?"

No sooner had he thought of his home when a bag of gold appeared upon the table. He put the money into his coat-pocket and called, "Iron, Steel, Strongest-of-all, come with me." And the dogs followed him as he retraced his path homeward.

His sister was pleased to hear of his good fortune and made ready to return with him at once, but cast ugly looks at the dogs.

When they returned to the palace, they found it still deserted. This time Maria insisted that she could cook better meals and took over the kitchen. Now Pietro and his dogs spent all day outdoors, returning only for the evening meal and to sleep.

One day while Maria was banging pots and pans in the kitchen she heard heavy footsteps and the loud thumping of a cane. She went to the stairs and called out, "Who is it? What do you want here?"

"Impertinent one," the voice of an old man answered, "don't you know that this house is mine?"

Being neither so kind nor so polite as her brother, she answered rudely, "I know nothing. My brother brought me here, so don't start a quarrel with me."

"Very well," said the old man, "he shall be made to pay for this with his life."

"All right, but don't blame me," she said indifferently.

The old man took out a tiny paper package from his pocket. "If you would like to live alone in this palace," he said craftily, "put this powder into your brother's supper. I shall return tomorrow."

The wicked sister did as the old man ordered. But when the dogs came into the house they rushed into the kitchen, ran to the hearth and overturned the pot of stew bubbling there so that not a morsel remained.

Maria was furious, but her good-hearted brother thought she was upset because his supper had been spoiled, so he soothed her, saying, "Never mind. It is the fault of my capricious dogs. We can eat some bread and cheese, which is what we are used to anyway."

The old man returned the next morning, but he knew without her telling him what had happened, for he was a wizard. He gave her another powder and told her to put it in her brother's wine.

She tried a second time to poison his wine, but the dogs tipped over the cask before he could fill his glass and once more saved their master's life.

When the old man returned the third time he said, "So long as those accursed dogs are here, we can do nothing to hurt their master." Then he gave her new instructions, and this is what the deceitful sister did: Just before it was time for her brother to return for supper, she got into bed and when he came in, pretended to be suffering from a severe headache. She told him she wanted to fix a cool drink for herself with a fresh lemon and asked him to pick one for her in the garden.

"Of course I'll do that for you," he said and called his dogs to accompany him as he always did. But before they could move, Maria shouted angrily, "Ah, those dogs of yours. You love them more than you do me. You can't be without them for a moment. Why don't you leave them here for once?"

"Don't be angry," he said soothingly. "I'll go down into the garden myself and pick the best lemon I can find for you."

As soon as her brother left the room, Maria got up, led the dogs into a room with barred windows and locked them in, as the old man had ordered.

Meanwhile, Pietro went down into the garden and, while looking for a fine lemon, was struck on the head and stunned. Turning around and seeing only an old man, he thought he would be able to defend himself. But he had no weapon and the old man rained so many blows upon him that all he could do, with what breath he had left, was to call his dogs. The poor dogs were helpless but, on hearing their master's desperate cries, struggled so hard that they were able at last to break through the bars on the windows and leap to his rescue. They quickly drove the old man away and he fled with his coat in tatters.

After caressing his loyal dogs and treating their wounds, Pietro faced his sister. By then he realized that she had betrayed him and he said to her sadly, "I went away from our father's house with only a bag of bread and my three dogs and left you there as mistress. I shall do the same again, but this time, instead of a bag of bread, I shall take with me a bag of gold and my three dogs. You are welcome to the rest."

Then he took his money, his gun and once more called, "Iron, Steel, Strongest-of-all, let's go!"

The dogs did not have to be urged to leave Maria; they were already on the doorstep. They walked for many miles until they arrived in a beautiful seaport where, to their great surprise, they found everyone weeping, Pietro entered a baker's shop to ask why and the owner answered, "It is obvious that you are a stranger, or you would not ask. Well, we are plagued by a terrible sea serpent with seven heads who forces us to give him a maiden to eat each year. She is chosen by lot, and this year it is the turn of the king's daughter. So you can imagine our woe. The king has proclaimed that whoever can avert this disaster by killing the serpent may marry the princess and become king."

Pietro thanked the man and, calling his dogs, went down to the edge of the sea and challenged the serpent to combat. "Now," he said to his dogs, "is the time for you to show your worth."

The dogs understood what their master expected of them and threw themselves upon the beast. The serpent fought fiercely and wounded them, but they were finally the victors. Pietro left the serpent's body on the sand but cut out the seven tongues from the seven heads. Then he put them in his pocket and went to take a look at the beautiful princess who was supposed to be sacrificed to the sea serpent.

An ugly black Moor was the first to arrive on the beach after Pietro killed the serpent, and as no one else was there, he cut off the seven heads. Then he ran back to meet the slowly winding royal procession, shouting boldly, "Long live the king's daughter! She is saved! I have killed the serpent, and the king must keep his promise to me." He displayed the seven heads for all to see.

The poor princess, seeing the boaster whom she must now marry, almost wished she had been eaten by the serpent. But there was nothing for her to do but obey, and the court and city began three days of celebration before the wedding.

Pietro now devised a plan to outwit the Moor. He took lodgings near the royal palace, and when the banquet tables were laden with food, he told his dogs to race about and create a disturbance by breaking dishes and goblets and spoiling the feast.

After three days of this the king believed there must be some omen in the strange behavior of the dogs and demanded to know to whom they belonged. He sent a servant to order their master to appear before him, but the messenger returned with the answer: "Tell His Majesty if he wishes to see me he must come to me."

Although the king could have forced Pietro to come to him, his curiosity overcame his anger and he went.

"Who has taught you to disobey a call from a king?" he asked Pietro, and the youth answered simply, "If you were a king who kept his word, I would have come. But you make promises and do not keep them."

"And what promise have I made to you that I did not keep?" asked the king in astonishment. "I have never seen you before."

"You promised to give your daughter in marriage to whoever killed the serpent," answered Pietro, "but you are not keeping that promise."

At this, the king, even more dumbfounded, said, "But I am keeping my word even to the extent of giving my daughter in marriage to a Moor. He came to me with the seven heads of the serpent.

Then Pietro showed the serpent's seven tongues to the king and said, "I could not have cut these out had the serpent been alive, so please look at the seven heads for yourself to see if the tongues are still there." And of course they were not.

No on could have been more delighted by the disclosure of the Moor's trick than the beautiful young princess, who found in Pietro a husband much more to her liking. Now the feasting began all over again and a royal wedding took place after all. The young peasant was crowned the new king. If as a peasant Pietro loved his wonderful dogs, he loved them still more as a king, and his gratitude knew no bounds for the great service they had rendered.

Time passed and the young king and queen lived happily together. Then one morning they experienced their first sorrow. Their dogs left them and did not return. They sent out many search parties but to no avail, so finally they resigned themselves to their loss.

Then one day an ambassador came to the court to announce to the king that there were three vessels in port, on each of which was a great personage. These foreign dignitaries sent word that they wished to renew an old friendship with King Pietro. The king thought there must surely be some mistake, because as a peasant he had never enjoyed the friendship of any important people. But he sent a messenger to invite them to come to the palace.

There were two kings and an emperor, and when they greeted the young king they asked smilingly, "Don't you remember us?"

"It would be a little difficult for me to remember you," he answered, "as I have never seen you before."

"Ah, we never believed that you would forget your faithful companions," the three said together.

"Certainly you can't be Iron, Steel and Strongest-of-all!" said the bewildered Pietro.

"Yes, we are," they answered. "A villainous wizard turned us into dogs, and not until a peasant should be seated on a throne through our efforts could we return to our former selves. You were always a kind master to us, and we will always remain your allies. If you are ever in trouble, remember that there are two kings and an emperor who will come to your aid."

The distinguished guests stayed several days and a feast was given in their honor. When they departed at last, they all wished one another great happiness, which they enjoyed for many, many years.

THE MOTHER OF TIME

AND THE ENCHANTED BROTHERS

*   *   *   *   *   *   *   *   *   *

*   *   *   *   *   *   *   *   *   *

NCE long ago a mother gave birth to seven sons in succession. As there was only one year's difference in their ages, they were like the reeds of a Pan-pipe, one just a bit longer than the other. When they had reached their teens, they said one day to their mother, who was expecting another child, "We dearly want a little sister, dear Mamina. If your next baby is not a girl, we shall leave your nest and go wandering through the world."

Their mother prayed that the child would be a girl or that her sons would change their minds, for she was very unhappy at the thought of losing the seven jewels of her heart.

When it was about time for the baby to be born, the boys told their mother that they would watch for a sign from the hill opposite their house. "If it is a girl, put a spoon and distaff in the window, and we shall come back home and stay with you always. If it is another boy, put in a pen and an inkstand."

The mother's prayers were answered. She gave birth to a fine baby girl and immediately told the nurse to put the sign in the window. But the good woman was so excited over the mother's joy that she became confused and when the brothers, who were watching eagerly, looked up to the window they saw a pen and inkstand instead of the spoon and distaff that she had intended to put there. So they sadly set out to wander in the strange, wide world.

They roamed through many countries. For three years they could find no place to live or anyone who would give them a home. Finally they came to a beautiful forest with a singing river running through it and trees that seemed to be dancing to the rhythm of the waters. Here they found a blind ogre. As they were weary and famished, they asked him for a few crusts of bread. He said he would give them all the food they wanted and a home, if in return they would lead him about, each one in turn, for a day at a time. They accepted the ogre's offer gladly and for a while all went well.

Meanwhile, their sister, who had been christened Lucia, had grown into a lovely girl, but she was very unhappy. From the time she learned that her brothers were wandering about homeless in the world she had been able to think of little else. She longed to go in search of them, and gave her mother no peace until at last the poor woman consented and sent her off with prayers for her safety.

Lucia walked from place to place, asking everywhere for news of her seven brothers. At last she was directed to the very wood where the ogre lived and found his house in the middle of the forest. When she told her brothers who she was, they received her with great joy. Their happiness in the reunion was all the greater because of the cruel mistake that had separated them so long from her, and from their dear mother.

They made Lucia at home, but warned her to be careful lest the ogre discover that she was in the house. He had been blinded long ago by a woman who had plucked out his eyes while he was asleep. Now he hated women so much that he devoured every one he could lay his hands on. They also warned her to share everything she ate with the cat; otherwise the animal would do her harm. She even made a little game of feeding the cat. Every time she shared a morsel of anything with it, she would say, "This for me, that for you, and this for the king's daughter."

One morning the ogre stayed at home and sent the boys out hunting. While Lucia was cleaning some chick-peas to cook for her brothers' dinner, she found a hazelnut in the basket and without remembering to share it with the cat, she popped it into her mouth. Immediately the little animal put out the fire.

Upset over this blunder, Lucia made a second one, even worse. The fire had gone out and she, wanting to kindle another one, thoughtlessly ran upstairs to the ogre's room and

asked him for a brand. As soon as he heard her voice, he
called out to her, "Wait a moment, and I shall give you what
you're looking for!" But she noticed that instead of going
toward the fire, he was sharpening a huge knife. Terrified
and remembering her brothers' warning, she seized a fire-
brand, ran downstairs and locked herself in her room. Soon
the ogre followed and beat furiously on the door.

In the midst of the commotion the brothers returned,
whereupon the ogre reproached them angrily for hiding an
enemy in his house. Giangrazio, the oldest and most sensible
of the boys, tried to calm the ogre. "We know nothing about
any woman being in the house," he told him. "She must have
come in while we were out hunting. But if you want to catch
her, I shall take you into our rooms from the rear, where she
cannot escape you." But instead of leading the ogre to their
rooms, he took him to a deep pit, pushed him down to the
bottom, and he and his brothers filled the pit with earth.

Giangrazio then scolded his sister, "You must be more
careful to obey us in the future. You might have lost your
life had we not returned in time. Now listen carefully, Lucia.
You must never, never, under any circumstance, pick anything that grows near or on the grave of the ogre. If you do,
the seven of us will be turned into doves."

"May heaven preserve me from bringing such a misfortune
upon us all!" promised Lucia. "I shall be very, very careful."

With the ogre out of the way, the brothers took possession
of the entire house and they lived there happily together
with their sister. Since it was winter they decided to wait
for good spring weather to start out on their long homeward
journey.

But before they attained their hearts' desire, they were to experience more trouble. One day while the brothers were out cutting wood for the winter fires, an old pilgrim passed their house. He mocked a monkey sitting high on a pine branch and it retaliated by throwing a pinecone down on the old man's head. Lucia heard his cries and ran out to see what caused them. Filled with pity and forgetting everything but her impulse to help the unfortunate pilgrim, she picked some rosemary leaves from the ogre's grave to boil with soft bread and salt for a poultice. Then she bound the old man's head, gave him food and sent him on his way.

That evening, as she was setting the table for supper, seven doves flew in and she recognized Giangrazio's voice as he reproached her, "Better had your hand been cut off before you picked those accursed leaves from the ogre's grave. Now we shall not be able to return home as we planned, but we will have to live always near the sea, a prey to other winged creatures, animals and hunters. To save the head of an old man, you have sacrificed the heads of your seven brothers. The only way to undo the harm you have done and enable us to return to our human form is for you to find the Mother of Time."

Poor Lucia was crestfallen. She begged her brothers' forgiveness and promised she would never rest but would journey on to the end of the world until she found the old Mother. She lost no time in starting out on her search. Taking tender leave of her poor winged brothers, she admonished them to keep safely indoors until her return so that no harm might befall them.

In her eagerness to help her brothers, she walked very fast

and soon reached the sea. As she hurriedly passed a big whale on the shore, he said to her, "Where are you running, my beautiful maid?"

And she answered, "I am looking for the house of the Mother of Time."

"Follow the shore," said the whale, "and turn inland at the first river you see. From there someone else will tell you where to go. When you find the old Mother, will you do me a favor? Please ask her what I can do to be able to swim in safety. I am constantly being hurled against the rocks or thrown upon the seashore."

"I shall do my best for you," said Lucia, and she thanked the whale and hurried off.

She walked for what seemed to her a very long time before she found the river. Then she followed its course inland until she came to a beautiful green plain, covered with bright wild flowers. There a little mouse said to her, "Lovely child, where are you going all alone in this wild country?" And she replied, "I am looking for the house of the Mother of Time."

"You still have far to go," said the kindly little mouse, "but do not be discouraged, for there is an end to everything in this world. Go on toward the mountains you see rising before us, and there someone else will direct you. When you find the old Mother, will you be good enough to ask her how we poor little mice can free ourselves from the tyranny of cats? If you will bring me that information, you may count me as your slave forever."

"You are a very good little mouse," said Lucia, "and I shall try to return your kindness," and she hastened off toward her goal.

The mountains were almost farther away than they had seemed when she started, and Lucia was beginning to wonder if she would ever reach them. She sat down to rest a bit, and noticed an army of ants going underground with loads of grain on their backs. "Where are you going, my child?" one of them asked, "and who are you?"

"I am an unfortunate girl," replied Lucia, "for I have made a serious mistake and now I must find the Mother of Time in order to ask her how I can set it right."

"Keep on going," directed the ant, "until you reach a valley in an opening of the mountains. When you arrive there, ask your way again, and when you find Mother Time, will you do me a kindness? Be good enough to ask her what we ants can do to extend our lives. It seems to me a waste of energy for us to have to store up such a lot of food that we may not even live to eat—especially since we are so small and are extinguished as rapidly as a candle in the wind."

"I shall not forget your request," Lucia answered the ant, and off she went again.

At last Lucia reached the valley in the opening of the mountains. After walking for a long time, she came to an ancient oak tree. "Why are you rushing so breathlessly, my pretty maid?" the tree asked. "Do sit down to rest for a while in the shade of my branches."

Lucia thanked the oak for its kind invitation but explained why she could not stop.

When the oak heard of her destination, it said, "You are almost there. Another day's journey will bring you to the house of the Mother of Time, high on the mountain. But if you are as kind as you are lovely, I beg of you not to forget to ask the old Mother how I can recover my lost glory. Once upon a time, my acorns provided food for great men; now I am only food for pigs."

"Be sure that I shall do my best for you," said Lucia and hurried on her way.

When she had gone a little farther, she came to a tall mountain, poking its snowy head into the clouds. At the foot of it an old man was lying on some straw, the same old man whose head Lucia had bandaged outside the ogre's house. He looked up and recognized the girl, and when she told him what had happened to her brothers and where she was going and why, he was very sorry to hear that he had caused so much trouble and offered to help her all he could in return for her kindness to him.

"I have to see Father Time myself," said the old pilgrim. "I must pay him some money for the rent of land of his that I have cultivated. But I am too old to climb that mountain, so I shall wait down here to settle accounts with his clerks. He is a terrible tyrant and exacts tribute from everyone, especially from men of my age. But I know how to deal with the rascal, and shall tell you what to do.

"Now, listen to me carefully, my pretty child. At the top of this mountain you will find a house, built before the time of men. Everything about it is crumbling except the coat of arms over the door. Look carefully at this door, which bears a carved phoenix, the symbol of resurrection. Inside the house are files, saws, scythes and pruning hooks and hundreds of cauldrons filled with ashes and labeled with the names of once-proud cities long since gone, cities like Carthage, Corinth and Troy. But Time keeps their ashes in memory of his triumphs.

"When you approach the house, hide yourself until you see Time come out. Then go in and you will see his mother, who has a chin that reaches to the ground and a hump so high that you cannot see the top of it. Her hair falls down to her feet like a dapple-gray horse's tail, and her wrinkled face is as stiff as a starched shirt-front. She sits on a clock fastened to the wall. As her eyes are hooded by heavy eyelids, she will not be able to see you. So go straight up to the clock and take out its weights. Then call the old woman and beg her to grant you your wishes. She will call her son, but since he cannot move a step while the weights are off the clock she will be obliged to give you whatever information you want of her. However, if she begins to bargain with you, do not trust her promises, unless she swears by the wings of her son. When she does that you will be safe in doing whatever she asks of you."

As the old man finished speaking, he vanished before Lucia's eyes. The poor girl left him with a prayer for the repose of his soul.

Hurrying still more to make up for the delay, Lucia reached the top of the mountain, quite out of breath. There she hid and watched for Father Time to leave the house. Finally he came flying out. He was a very old, old man, with a long gray beard. His coat, too, was very old, with tiny labels bearing the names of various persons sewn onto it. He had large wings and moved so fast that he was out of sight in a jiffy. When Lucia entered the ruined house, she was frightened by its disorder, but she walked bravely up to the clock and took the weights out. Then she made her requests to the old Mother, who shrieked and called to her son. It was just what Lucia had expected, so she said calmly, "You can call as much as you like but your son will not come to you, for I have the weights of the clock in my hands."

The old Mother, finding herself powerless, said to Lucia coaxingly, "My dear, you must put those weights back and not hinder my son in his course. That is something that no human being has yet done. If you will do as I ask, I swear to you by the liquid with which my son corrodes everything that heaven will protect you and no harm will come to you."

"You are only wasting my time," said Lucia. "You will have to swear by something far more convincing to make me give up these weights."

"Then I swear to you by the teeth that gnaw every mortal thing," she said, "that if you will give them up, I shall tell you everything you want to know."

"That is still not sufficient," replied Lucia. "I know you are deceiving me."

"Well, then," said the old Mother in desperation, "I swear to you by the wings that hover over all things that I shall please you even more than you imagine."

Upon hearing that oath, Lucia put the weights into the old Mother's wrinkled hands and kissed them. This gave the woman so much pleasure that she said to her kindly, "Hide yourself behind this door, and when Time returns I will get him to answer all your questions. He never stays long, and when he leaves, you can slip out. But be careful that he does not hear you or see you."

Lucia did as she was told. Soon Time bounded in and began nibbling at everything, even the bits of plaster on the walls. When he was about to leave, his mother repeated all of Lucia's questions, which she begged him to answer for the sake of the milk with which she had nursed him as a baby.

He was reluctant to stop so long, but she entreated him until at last he consented, and this is what he said:

'The oak should be told that man will never respect it so long as it keeps treasures hidden under its roots. There is no way of freeing mice from cats unless the cats will consent to wearing a bell around their necks to announce their coming. Ants put on wings when they are about to die, so if they would abstain from flying they could prolong their lives to a hundred years. The whale should feast and make merry with the sea-rat, who will guide and keep him on the right path. And as for the doves, they will be able to return to their former state as soon as they sit on the horn of plenty.'

Having finished, Time rushed out to continue his race.

Lucia took leave of old Mother Time and, after thanking her for her great kindness, started on her way back. She reached the foot of the mountain at the same time as her seven brother-doves. They had been following in her wake ever since she left the house and only now had found her. As they were very tired, they alighted on the horns of an ox to rest. But no sooner had they touched the horns than they were transformed into the same handsome youths they had been before. They were greatly surprised until Lucia told them what Time had said. Then they understood that the ox's horns were a symbol of plenty.

After much rejoicing, and a little rest, they started back over the same road that Lucia had traveled. The first of her friends they encountered was the oak. Lucia reported what Time had said about the treasure, so it told the brothers to dig below its roots at once and to take for themselves whatever they found. After digging down very deep, they dis-covered a large jug filled with goldpieces which they divided into eight equal piles. Happy over their good fortune, each carried his own bundle and walked on until all were too tired to take another step. Then they lay down under a roadside hedge and fell asleep, with their bundles under their arms.

Just then a gang of robbers came by. Seeing the young people sound asleep, they tied their hands and feet to some trees and made off with the goldpieces. In the morning Lucia and her brothers awoke, only to lament their misfortune. Although the robbers did not kill them, their lives were still in danger from wild beasts and lack of food, for there was no way that they could untie themselves. While they were discussing how they could possibly get free, the little mouse came along. When it heard what Time had to say to the question it had asked, the grateful mouse nibbled Giangrazio's ropes. As soon as he was freed he was able to cut the ropes of his brothers and sister and they all set out on the road once more.

After walking for some time, they met the ant, to whom Lucia conveyed Time's reply. The ant thanked her and asked, "But why are you so pale and sad?" So she told her of their robbery and fright.

"Well," said the ant, "now I see how I can return one good deed for another. While I was carrying a load of grain underground, I saw the place where the robbers buried their stolen goods. I shall show you the site and you can help yourself to what is rightfully yours."

They followed the ant and retrieved all their stolen goldpieces, and continued on to the sea. There they found the whale, who was happy to receive the answer to the question he had asked Lucia. As they stood there talking, they saw that the robbers were pursuing them, armed to the teeth.

"This time we are really lost," they cried. "We cannot possibly get away from them and they will surely kill us."

"But you forget that I am here," said the whale. "In return for your sister's great kindness to me, I shall save you if you will mount my back."

As they were now really between the devil and the deep sea, they had no choice, however much they feared riding on a whale's back. But the whale avoided the rocks and brought them safely as far as the Bay of Naples, where they were picked up by a fishing boat and taken ashore.

From there they walked home and were received with great affection by their mother. She had suffered greatly during the absence of her children and was overjoyed that they were now reunited. It was another testament, she told them, to the wisdom of the old saying, "Do all the good you can, and forget you have done it."

PART TWO

A

LEGENDARY LAND

* * *

THE FOUNTAIN

OF ARETHUSA

* * * * * * * * * *

* * * * * * * * * *

ALONG the waterfront of the large harbor of Siracusa, a city founded by the Greeks in Sicily, is an ever-flowing symbol of true love. The Fountain of Arethusa, whose name comes from an old legend of a nymph and her lover, is not a fountain made by the hand of man, but a magical spring or deep well within a semi-circle of rocky gray walls. White ducks swim among slender papyrus plants in its clear blue-green waters.

Once upon a time there lived a beautiful nymph, Arethusa, who was devoted to Diana, goddess of the hunt. She cared nothing for men's glances or compliments; her one passion was hunting and she desired only praise as a huntress.

123

One day as she was walking through the woods after a wild chase, she came upon a cool, inviting stream. She sank down upon its grassy bank, dangling her feet in the rippling water and watching in it the reflection of the overhanging willows and the quicksilver, darting fish. Then, seeing no one about, she slipped off her garments and swam in it happily. After a while, as she lay floating, she became aware of a voice coming up from the depths of the river. Frightened, she fled to the nearest bank.

The voice followed her, murmuring, "Why do you flee from me, lovely maid? I am Alpheus, god of this river that bears my name. Fear me not, Arethusa. I love you, I love you. You are so beautiful!"

Arethusa stopped neither to dress nor to answer him. She sped like a deer through the woods, with Alpheus in pursuit. He was the stronged and gained ground. When he was about to catch up to her, she cried to Diana, "Save me, O goddess!"

Diana heard her anguished cry and wrapped so thick a cloud around her that Alpheus could not see her, even though he was within an inch of touching her more than once. But being unable to find her, he cried despairingly, "Arethusa, Arethusa, where are you?"

At hearing his voice, she trembled with fear, as though some wild beast were about to devour her. Then as she stood there shrinking, she felt as though she were dissolving in a mist. Her hair and her very bones seemed to be flowing down in streams, pools of water were forming where her feet had stood; she had indeed become a fountain.

In this form Alpheus was able to recognize her and, being a river god, he turned himself into water and wanted nothing more than to mix his waters for eternity with hers. So she appealed to Diana once again and the goddess cleft the earth and made a tunnel in it for her. Arethusa sped through it under the ocean and came up onto the Island of Ortygia, where Siracusa now stands, as a fountain of sweet water.

But Alpheus still pursued her. Now, however, since she had given up the sport of hunting, Arethusa gradually became more feminine. Her heart grew tender, and in time she returned Alpheus' love. She permitted him to mingle his waters with hers and the two lovers were happily united forever beneath the earth.

THE RETURN

OF THE SPRING

*   *   *   *   *   *   *   *   *   *

*   *   *   *   *   *   *   *   *   *

HE ancient town of Enna in the center of Sicily has another name, The Belvedere, or "lookout tower," for it is situated on a high rock almost on the very top of the world. From its ramparts a range of mountain peaks can be seen, with that of fiery Mount Etna rising above them all. The surrounding land is rich and fertile, with fields of corn and wheat, green pastures, vineyards, almond groves, trees, bushes and wild flowers.

Long, long ago when the Greeks occupied Enna, they built a temple on a rock dedicated to Cerere, goddess of agriculture and to all the good things that grow on earth. They also honored her beautiful daughter Persephone, the lovely goddes of spring, by a temple, some of the columns of which may be found in Enna's medieval cathedral. Eucalyptus trees still sway around Lake Pergusa and lilies and violets line its banks, where once spring reigned perpetually.

The goddess Cerere occasionally permitted her only daughter, the beautiful young Persephone, to spend the day in the woods on the shores of Lake Pergusa. She and a group of fair nymphs would amuse themselves happily by picking flowers, weaving them into garlands, singing and dancing.

As night fell, Cerere would arrive in her chariot to fetch her home again.

One day Persephone wandered deep into the woods away from her companions to pick some flowers. Her attention was attracted by a wondrous narcissus and she wandered still farther. As she reached out to pluck the blossom, she felt strong arms enfolding her. Her captor was none other than Pluto, Lord of the Underworld, who, having just come up to ɛarth through a deep cavern, forgot everything else at the sight of Persephone with her apron filled with lilies and violets—and she herself lovelier than any flower. He vowed she must be his queen and, holding her firmly beside him in his chariot, drove rapidly back to his realm.

The frightened Persephone was grieved to lose her armful of flowers, for she was still very much a child. Pluto only urged his black steeds to greater speed, calling each one by name and loosening his copper-colored reins. When he arrived at the River Cyane, the water nymph Cyane was surprised to see the dark-robed god with the girl. Her heart went out to Persephone and she tried to halt him by causing the stream to overflow its banks. But the powerful Pluto only struck the earth and it opened up a passage to his kingdom. And, to punish Cyane for daring to interfere, he turned her into a fountain. However, before the chariot disappeared beneath the earth, Persephone called to the friendly Cyane, "Please tell my dear mother where I am being taken!" And, as she spoke, she quickly loosened her girdle and threw it to Cyane.

When Cerere returned to the woods at nightfall she found Persephone gone. Her companions could not tell her what had become of her, so she immediately set out in search of her beloved child. Her grief was so great that she could not rest, eat or sleep. At first she searched through every orchard, cave, and town near Enna. Then she went on and on, even to other countries, crossing the sea, lakes, rivers, mountains, valleys, cities and villages. But nowhere could she find any trace of her dear Persephone. So she returned again, sadly, to Sicily.

One day she sat down to rest near the Fountain of Cyane, and the passage Pluto had hewn for himself to his own land. As she sat there sorrowing, she noticed a familiar object floating among the papyrus plants. It was Persephone's girdle, which Cyane had kept and now gently wafted toward her. She would have given Cerere Persephone's message, but she dared not speak for fear of provoking further Pluto's wrath.

Cerere picked up the girdle with loving hands but without joy, for here was proof that a tragic fate had befallen her child. She could not guess what it was, so she blamed the land of Sicily for her loss, and punished it. She caused a burning hot sun to dry up the earth. Seeds failed to sprout and cattle died. More disasters might have succeeded these had the goddess not chanced to speak one day to another nymph, who had been turned into the Fountain of Arethusa.

"Dear goddess," pleaded Arethusa, "do not make this innocent land and its inhabitants suffer for your sorrow. They had no part in your daughter's disappearance. But I have seen her and can tell you where she is."

Then Arethusa told Cerere that when her waters had flowed through the lower regions of the earth, she had seen Persephone on the throne next to the haughty Pluto. She looked regal in her long black robe and golden crown, Arethusa said, but sad at having been so long separated from her mother and the earth, without sunshine or flowers or the song of birds. All that grew in the shadows of the underworld were some dark poppies and bright red pomegranates near a black river.

Cerere, dumbfounded, immediately besought Jupiter to restore her child. He told her he would do so provided Persephone had not taken any food during her stay and sent Mercury, his swift messenger, along with green-robed Spring, to command Pluto to liberate Persephone. The cunning Pluto said he would comply with Jupiter's request, but in the meanwhile he had deliberately offered the unsuspecting Persephone some ripe pomegranates from which she had sucked the sweet pulp. Thus Persephone was thenceforth to spend half the year with Pluto and half with her mother.

Cerere had to make the best of a bad bargain, but she was happy to be able to take her child into her arms once more

and to have her for even half the year. Thus she made peace with the land of Sicily and restored it to favor. It became fertile once again, clothed in the beauty of its golden fields of corn and wheat, its almond and fruit orchards, its flowers and flowering trees and bushes, its sunshine and rains. And whenever Persephone returned to live with her mother, all the green plants blossomed in her honor. Thus for the people she personified spring and summer and became the beloved goddess of these happy seasons.

PRINCESS SICILIA

AND THE SHEPHERD

*   *   *   *   *   *   *   *   *   *

*   *   *   *   *   *   *   *   *   *

NCE upon a time a king and queen of a country in the Orient had an only daughter whom they guarded like a jewel. Her name was Sicilia and she was as beautiful as the sun. They loved her so much that they could not bear to think of her marrying—not even the son of King Solomon. But not even a king may see over the horizon of tomorrow, and his beloved daughter was soon to roam the earth as an exile.

One day a dusty traveler with a little owl tied by its feet to his pilgrim's staff, passed by the palace and saw the wistful Princess Sicilia in the garden. "O daughter of the king, can you spare two small pieces of fruit?" he asked.

She gave him a basket overflowing with grapes, peaches, almonds and pistachio nuts. "May these strengthen you as you travel about the world," she said. "I would like to see what lies over the garden wall."

"Thank you, little queen. Perhaps you will," he said mysteriously and took his leave of her.

Just then the king appeared. "What did that old fellow want," he asked the housekeeper.

"He is one who can foretell the future," was the reply.

"Pilgrim, turn back!" called the king.

"At your service, Your Majesty," said the old man, returning.

"Here are seven golden coins if you will reveal to me my daughter's destiny," said the king.

The old man smoothed his beard, put on a pair of spectacles and placed his staff against the trunk of an olive tree. He took the princess's hand, turned it over and studied her palm, but remained silent.

"Are you dumb?" asked the king. "Can't you speak?"

"Your Majesty, there are words that dry up the tongue," answered the wizard. "I would say all that I have read in her hand, but I do not know how you will take it."

"You are at liberty to express your thoughts," said the king. They walked along a few paces together so as to be out of earshot of the princess, who had run blithely through the garden in pursuit of a bright butterfly.

"Well, then," began the old man, "a great danger awaits your daughter. I see a black cloud hovering over her, on which a mandril baboon is looking for her on land and sea. Within seven years he will come to your palace and nothing will stop him—neither soldiers, nor priests, nor the sea, nor the mountains with all their rocks!"

The astonished king could not bring himself to speak, but turned abruptly and returned to the palace.

That night he was quite unable to sleep. He tossed and turned and turned and tossed. Finally he said angrily to the queen, "What is the matter with this mattress tonight? It is as hard as rocks."

"How can that be, Your Majesty?" said she, "it is made of downy canary feathers. Shall I summon the housekeeper?"

"No, it doesn't matter," he said. "Do you believe that what a fortune-teller sees in your hand will come to pass?"

"Certainly I do," answered the queen.

"Know then," he told her, "that our daughter's life is in grave danger. In seven years she is to be claimed by a mandril baboon now seeking her by land and sea."

"And you tell me this news so calmly," cried the queen, "even complaining about the mattress being hard! There is no time to lose. Let us put her out of harm's reach at once!"

"But we have seven years yet," said the king.

"No, we have no time to lose. We must act immediately!" answered the queen.

So they arose and awakened their daughter. They took her down to the beach and put her aboard a ship laden with all sorts of household objects, money, jewels, bread, wine, fruit and water. At dawn they raised the sails of the ship to send her off across the sea—far from any abductor.

"Father, Mother, where must I go?" asked the bewildered young girl. They did not want to frighten her by telling her of the mysterious baboon. "It is for the best," they said. "We would like to keep you near us, but in order to save your life you must follow the sun. When you come to an island which has a mountain with snow on its peak and fire within, you should land there because only where snow and fire meet can the enchantment that has been cast upon you be broken."

The bewildered Sicilia took leave of her sorrowing parents and sailed away. The first island she reached was shaped like the open wing of a hawk and was bleak and barren. So she did not stop but sailed on and on, following the path of the sun, passing Africa and Malta. One moonlit night she saw a glowing red point in the sky which grew larger and

larger. At dawn she saw a mountain that looked like a
column of the sky. Clouds of snow covered its peak like a
cape. Surely this was where snow and fire mingled!

Here she dropped anchor and went ashore. She wandered
about its slopes for hours gazing at the lovely valleys, the
tree-shaded riverbanks. Finally, in desperation, she called out
and a youth appeared from a cave. He was wearing a lamb-
skin coat, with the wool on the outside, as shepherds do
even now in Sicily.

"What are you doing here?" he asked the lovely stranger
in wonder. "Are you alone in the world?"

She told him that she had been exiled to seek a mountain
with snow on its peak and fire within.

They went down to her ship together and she showed him
her jewels and the varied objects her father had put aboard
the ship, among which was a golden object made in the form
of a hawk's wing. "What is this?" asked the shepherd curi-
ously, for he knew nothing of the ways of farmers or artisans.

"This is a ploughshare," she explained. "And here are an
anvil and a hammer. With them you can bend iron and
make weapons that will defend you from the wolves better
than night fires." She showed him also a small golden pitcher.
"This is a pitcher in which you can capture raindrops or
milk from your herds."

The shepherd, in return, proudly showed her his herds and
pastures, the forests and fields of rick black earth.

"This whole island will be yours if you will share it with
me," he said. She accepted happily and they decided to
build a house with the tools she had brought on the slopes
of the mountain of snow and fire.

In the springtime the fruit-trees blossomed and the crops they had sown grew as tall as a man on horseback, and the fields of ripening grain were even more beautiful than the golden crowns the young couple wore as they walked among them. "What shall we call this fair land?" asked the shepherd.

The princess thought a while and answered, "I shall give it my own name—Sicily!"

And from then on the lovely Island of Sicily took on the radiance of the princess who gave it her name, and it, too, became as beautiful as the sun.

THE BEAUTIFUL WEAVER

AND THE GOLDEN SHELL

* * * * * * * * * *

* * * * * * * * * *

N Palermo many years ago everyone knew of Maria, the weaver's daughter, who was as expert as her father in making the finest of cloth. Merchants from Greece, Africa, Spain and other Mediterranean countries came to their humble house at the foot of Monte Pellegrino to buy the fine silk and wool they made. Maria was so beautiful that even the stars were jealous of her; some of them would not come out at night until she had gone to bed for fear that no one would look at them.

Many sought her hand in marriage. One of her suitors boasted, "I have fought alone against a hundred." Another said, "I have won the weapons of five barons." And still another bragged, "The king and I are like brothers."

But the wise Maria, although young, knew how to judge men as well as she knew her loom, so she chose the quiet standard-bearer of the king, who made no vain boasts but said manfully, "Fear I quell as often as it rises within me. Maria, I want you for my wife." And Maria was happy to become his betrothed.

But the fame of Maria's beauty had reached the ear of the King of Tunis and he sent a ship to Palermo. "If you bring back the girl you shall have as much gold as she weighs," he admonished the captain. "If you return without her you will be tied to a chain as heavy as yourself."

When the ship arrived at Palermo, the clever captain disguished himself as a merchant and went straight to the weaver's house. He carried silver belts, rings, earrings and pearls and called, "Silver, fine silver work to sell!"

"O stranger, won't you come in!" Maria herself opened the door, and the captain thought to himself it was not possible that a girl could be so beautiful. He gave her one of his finest silver belts and two large fine pearls in exchange for two pieces of sky-blue silk.

"Would you like anything else?" he asked. Then he said, "Are you alone?"

"There is no one else at home; but I'm not alone, for I'm with God," she answered simply.

The captain finished measuring the silk, which fell in a heap at his feet, and asked Maria to help him fold it. But when she bent down to pick up one end, he threw a cloak over her and hurried to his ship with his precious burden. She could not cry out or even make the sign of the cross, enfolded as she was in a cocoon of blue silk.

The ship left port and sailed straight for Tunis. The wind helped, but it was the wind of the devil, for when there is harm to be done, he comes from far away to blow. The city disappeared from view, the trees looked smaller, but Monte Pellegrino still stood in silhouette between the blue sea and the blue sky.

Maria was left free. "She is not a sparrow, so she cannot fly away," thought the captain. But feathers and wings are not the only means of escape and Maria jumped into the sea. A sailor jumped in after her, but she eluded his grasp and swam away. Disappearing under the waves, she went down, down until she reached the rocks at the very bottom of the sea, where she knocked at an iron door. It was opened slowly by invisible hands.

She found herself in a watery palace in which were stored all the treasures swallowed through the ages by the waves—mountains of gold and silver and precious gems. She wandered through corridors as long and wide as rivers and finally came to a corner where a hundred-year-old tortoise sat. "Poor girl," it said gloomily, "you have fallen into the hands of the god of the sea. If you don't pay the ransom, you will become a tortoise like me, or a shrub of coral or an oyster."

"What must I pay?" asked Maria.

"Three golden lions, three rods, three columns and three boats of fine gold."

"But where would my father get all that gold?" wailed the girl. "I may as well resign myself to my fate."

"It is all very well for me," said the tortoise, "but if one is as young and beautiful as you and is betrothed to an officer of the king, it would be better to return to the world before the first wrinkles begin to crease your brow."

"Who will go to tell my father where I am?" asked Maria.

The tortoise called to a sea urchin, which was immediately transformed into a fisherman, with a gray beard and a gold earring in his right ear. He wore a deep blue shirt, a cap with a hawk's head, and his trousers were turned up.

The tortoise told this strange-looking fisherman, "Go up to Palermo and ask for the ransom for this girl."

The old man left and quickly reached the house at the foot of Monte Pellegrino. The door was opened by Maria's father and the fisherman asked him, "Are you the weaver who has lost a daughter?"

"I would rather be dead than have to say yes," he answered.

"Well, she is in a palace at the bottom of the sea," said the messenger. "If you pay the sea god's ransom, she will be returned to you."

"How much?" asked the weaver anxiously.

"Three golden lions, three rods, three columns and three boats of fine gold," said the fisherman.

"Where shall I get all that gold?" asked the weaver despairingly. "I have heard of fairies and wizards who can do anything and everything with their magic, but where shall I find them? Look, if I were to sell my house, my garden, my loom and all that I possess I could not fill even a small pot with gold. You could have saved yourself the trouble of coming here only to add to my sorrow."

So the sailor returned to the palace at the bottom of the sea, where the tortoise and Maria were waiting for him and reported, "I have done your bidding, and the answer is the same as all relatives give upon being asked for such an impossible ransom."

Maria expected such an answer and was quite ready to be turned into a shrub of coral, or an oyster or to go on living at the bottom of the sea as a tortoise. But her friend the tortoise would not give up hope of securing the ranson for the beautiful girl.

They went into a room as large as a lake, where a fire was burning in the hearth. The tortoise touched one of the embers and it turned into a man.

"Go up to Palermo," commanded the tortoise, "and find the

standard-bearer of the king and tell him his fiancée is in a palace at the bottom of the sea and that the sea god will not release her unless he pays the ransom."

The messenger went to the royal palace, but the guards would not let him enter until he opened his cloak and showed them his golden belt and his sword that shone like the sun. He found his way to the standard-bearer and said to him, "Your promised bride is a prisoner in a palace at the bottom of the sea. If you do not pay the ransom you will never see her again. The sea god asks for three golden lions, three rods, three columns and three boats of fine gold."

"Wait for me," said the standard-bearer and he went to the king.

"Your Majesty, will you make war on the king of Tunis?" he asked him. "He is immensely rich and he possesses much good land that if you plant the handle of a lance it grows into a tree."

"I'm sorry," answered the king, "but I make war only when it pleases me."

"Then will Your Majesty give me leave? I must go away for a long time."

"It is granted," answered the king.

The standard-bearer went to where the messenger was waiting and said to him, "Even if I were to sell myself as a slave I should not get enough gold for the ranson. So if Maria is to remain a prisoner, I want to be with her and am willing to be turned into a rock, a fish, or anything the sea god wishes."

So they went down together to the palace at the bottom of the sea. On the way, an old man as old as the wind appeared before them in a boat that came out of a whirlpool,

and he said to the standard-bearer, "When the heart is rich in love, it always finds a way. Because of your generous spirit, I shall free your fiancée, and my wedding gift to you both will be the ransom. Go to her and be happy!"

At that moment a ship appeared with Maria on it, followed by another bearing three golden lions, three rods and three columns, and towing three boats of fine gold. The ship itself was of gold, its hull, its anchors and even its sails. The faithful standard-bearer mounted a golden ladder to join his Maria, and they sailed toward Palermo, where they were married and lived long and happily.

The radiance of all that gold colored the curve of mountains surrounding Palermo so that to this day the city is called "La Conca d'Oro," or "The Golden Shell."

COUNT ROGER

AND THE FATA MORGANA

* * * * * * * * * *

* * * * * * * * * *

VERY long time ago a Norman knight, Count Roger, led his army to Sicily to free the Christians from their pagan Saracen rulers. When they reached the province of Calabria they found a wealth of natural beauty. They crossed mountains from which they could see both the Ionian and Tyrrhenian Seas and marched through woods of stately pines, firs and elms, past groves of olive, almond and mulberry trees and broad fields. So dazzled were the soldiers that one of them said to the count, "I have heard it said that there is a paradise on earth for those who know where to find it. If that be true, then surely this is our paradise. Can we not remain here?"

Count Roger replied, "No, we must go on. After we win our battle against the Saracens to free our Christian brothers, we shall find another more beautiful paradise in Sicily."

They approached the Straits of Messina on a lovely, quiet moonlit night in which the south wind was laden with the fragrance of fruit trees in blossom. In the stillness they could hear warlike music and the lament of slaves in chains coming from Sicily across the Straits.

Count Roger asked a hermit, "What is the meaning of

153

those strange perfumes, the music and the laments we hear?"

The hermit answered, "The perfumes are from the flowering gardens and orchards of the Saracens, the music is a dance of victory, while their Christian slaves lament."

"Are there many Saracens?" asked the count.

"Yes, many, very many," replied the hermit. "There are great numbers of them and they know how to cultivate the soil, how to fight and to conquer. There is no cross on their flags, only a half-moon that looks like a scythe."

The next morning as they looked across to Sicily on the short of the Strait, Count Roger saw the Saracens driving long lines of camels, horses and cattle to the water's edge to drink, and he said to his knight, "What a pity to have ten thousand soldiers and not one ship! We cannot cross the sea in our saddles. I must have Sicily, even at the cost of twenty years of fighting. Now begins my Crusade!"

The Fata Morgana, in her palace at the bottom of the sea, heard his words and appeared before him in her enchanted carriage, drawn by seven white horses.

She was very beautiful, with a face like a cherry blossom, and eyes like fires in a dark wood. The count, who was young and handsome, was captivated by her beauty, but he fought against her spell even as he heard her musical voice saying, "I can take you to Sicily in my carriage if you wish."

"I shall go to fight my war in Sicily with my own horses and in my own ships," he replied haughtily, "not in an enchanted carriage."

The Fata Morgana beat the air three times with her wand and threw three stones into the sea. "Look!" she said.

Count Roger looked and saw a miracle. He saw the Island of Sicily approaching in the water, as in a mirror, with its cities, gardens, fields, seaports and mountains and the snow-clad peak of Mount Etna rising above them; it looked like a gem set in the Mediterannean. As he looked in amazement, he could discern olive, orange and every kind of fruit tree, fields of golden-ripe wheat and corn, many camels, oxen and other animals on the roads. And he saw clearly the beautiful city of Palermo, with its numerous palaces, gardens, fountains, and its harbor filled with ships.

As Count Roger stood in wonder, the fairy said to him, "Mount my carriage and you shall be king of all you behold!"

The count, hearing her speak, came to his senses and answered proudly, "Christ, not a fairy, will give me Sicily!"

Upon hearing the word "Christ," the fairy disappeared and all the wonders the count had been seeing went down to the bottom of the sea with her, leaving Sicily where it really was, far away.

Later Count Roger did get his ships, and, with Christian

flags flying and bugles sounding, he sailed across the sea to Sicily, where he established Norman rule.

The Fata Morgana is said to live still in her palace at the bottom of the sea, and at certain times and in a certain light, you can, like Count Roger, see distant parts of Sicily mirrored in the water from the beaches of the lovely city of Reggio in Calabria.

NICOLA

PESCE

* * * * * * * * * *

* * * * * * * * * *

NCE long ago in Sicily, in the time of King Frederick II, there lived a boy who was called "Fish" by everyone because he acted just like one in the ocean. Nicola Pesce could stay under water as long as he liked without coming up to breathe and, like a fish, he could dive in all sorts of deep places—even to the bottom of the most dangerous whirlpool in Italy.

The son of a poor Sicilian fisherman, he lived with his family on the shore of the Straits of Messina, the narrow body of water that separates the Island of Sicily from the mainland of Italy. As Nicola was the youngest of several brothers and could help his father the least, he was usually left at home to water their four jasmine plants and to help his mother sell the fish the others caught.

Nicola watered the plants with pleasure, but he hated selling the fish. Once when he was left with a basketful of colorful fish, he said to them pityingly, "Ah, if I were only a saint, I would surely revive you and toss you back into the sea."

And again, one Christmas, when eels are a popular holiday delicacy in Sicily, Nicola found a live eel in the basket and impulsively threw it back into the water. His mother saw him and ran up to him, shouting, "You wicked boy! Is this the way you throw away a gift of God? And now, when eels sell at their highest and the tax collectors take everything away and leave you only your eyes to weep with! May you also become a fish!"

It is said in Sicily that when parents reproach their children the heavens open and their words go straight to God. And, from that day on, Nicola practically lived in the sea. He was on or under the waves all morning and afternoon for whole days and nights at a time.

Nicola not only loved the fish but he also loved the blue-green water-world in which they dwelt. And because he could plunge deep into the sea among the fish, he saw many wonderful things. One day he ran into his house and shouted excitedly, "Mamina, I just saw a group of octopuses dance in a swirling pool of red carnations." Other times he would tell his mother about meadows of brilliant seaweed, gardens of coral, of sirens and their caves and of the changing colors of the water. "Their hues are like those we see in the sky," he told her in wonder, "the pink of dawn, the blue and gold of sunlight on a clear day, the flaming red of sunset, and sometimes the black of night."

His poor mother listened in terror. She did not believe such wonders existed, and thought he must be under the spell of some wicked witch. So she went into the hills to consult a hermit. The good man sympathized with her and told her to try several charms which should prevail against a witch's spell. First, she was to wash the boy's shirt in holy water, then tie a red band around his waist and put an acorn in his pocket. Also the hermit told her to give him bread made of a rye weed which occasionally has the power to make people forget.

But nothing could make Nicola forget the sea. His mother did everything the hermit told her to do, yet Nicola remained as attached to the sea as ever. For God had granted her angry wish uttered the day he had tossed the eel back into the sea that he also might become a fish.

As Nicola grew older he spent even more time in the sea. The waves were his sea-horses and he was more comfortable on their backs than he would have been on a soft feather bed. He swam to distant cities in Calabria and even to Naples, stopping at the cave of the winds of the Aeolian Isles to learn which way they would blow. When he tired of swimming, he would ride on the backs of big fish, who carried him willingly.

He knew all the ships and sailors by name, for they often gave him food and listened with interest to his wonderful tales of deep-sea life. On days when a storm came up, Nicola would hurry to any ship in need, battling with the winds to help the captain guide it to port. For the sea was his home, his world and he knew his way in it when it was rough as well as when it was calm.

Nicola soon learned how to bring up some of the objects he discovered at the bottom of the sea—sunken boats, anchors, chains, and one day a small barrel of gold coins. But though he and his family remained as poor as ever, his fame spread throughout the Mediterranean.

One year King Frederick II of Sicily made a long stay in Messina. His court, with its many courtiers, fine costumes, houses and carriages dazzled the people. They were also much moved by the kindness and beauty of his young daughter, Princess Margaret.

The king had heard of Nicola and wanted to see the youth. So the captain of the fortress offered to have the remarkable boy perform some of his underwater feats for him. But the king was not content with small things. He wanted to have a real test of the young man's ability. So off everyone went to the Faro, a lighthouse about which swirl the most dangerous waters in the world. He threw a golden goblet into the whirlpool and ordered Nicola to bring it back to him. Nicola dove without any hesitation and disappeared far beneath the foaming waters.

The crowd that had gathered around the king waited silently and anxiously and broke into applause when after a short time Nicola returned with the goblet held aloft. He handed it to the king with great dignity and at the same time asked leave to present a small branch of rosy sea coral to the princess. Princess Margaret had instantly admired the tall, slender youth and he, in turn, thought he had never seen anyone so serene and lovely as she.

The king was amazed at Nicola's first feat, which no other diver could possibly have duplicated, but he wished to test him still further. "Nicola," he said, "I want to know what my kingdom rests on. You are to swim around the island deep under the water. Then come and tell me what you have seen." Nicola bowed and dove again into the water.

As Nicola could cover long distances quickly he soon returned to the court. He was dressed in his poor fisherman's clothes, but his bearing was noble and he spoke fearlessly.

"Your Excellency," he said as he bent his knee before the king, "I have found that your kingdom rests on three col-

umns. Two of them are of granite and are as strong as mountains, but the third one, which is between Messina and Catanía, is in danger of collapsing. It is shrouded in purple darkness and surrounded by boiling water and flames, so that even the fish dare not approach it. I swam to where the fire and the water are battling for life. There I heard the creaking of the column and a voice saying at intervals, 'Now it falls. Now it falls!' "

Everyone was impressed by the young swimmer's account and by his valor, but the king was not yet satisfied. He did not believe that fire could be burning in the sea and wanted proof.

The next day the king, the princess, their attendants and a crowd of spectators met at the lighthouse, and once again they saw Nicola disappear in the whirlpool to bring back proof of the fire he claimed he had seen.

After an hour of anxious waiting, Nicola returned and stood before the king. Holding out his hands to show the burns on them, he said, "If I were St. Joseph I could have brought Your Majesty some of the fire in my cloak, but since I am not a saint this is the only proof I can bring."

The king insisted cruelly that he did not send him down to burn his hands but to bring back some of the fire, and added tauntingly, "So you're afraid!"

"Afraid?" repeated Nicola as he answered him proudly. "Those of us who live a life of danger do not know the word 'afraid.' I know I shall never come back, but let it be as you wish. Every man must die once."

Then Nicola went home to take leave of his parents. He did not want to worry them, so he behaved as though nothing unusual were going to happen. He watered the four jasmine plants and helped his father fix the rudder on his boat. As he was leaving he gave his mother the tiny coral branch he always carried in his pocket as a good-luck piece, for he knew he would never need it again.

Then he went to the sea and plunged down in the boiling waters to where the fire and water were mingled.

The princess was very unhappy while Nicola was going through his ordeals, but she dared not intercede for him lest her father guess that she was in love with a poor fisherman's son. But as the days passed and he did not return, she became ill with longing.

Finally she knew in her heart that she would never see her beloved again. She was standing on the seashore with one of the search parties that were looking for Nicola, when she heard his voice. It seemed to come from a whirlpool in the form of a red carnation, which said to her, "Don't expect to see me soon again. I must stay here at the heart of the fire. When I arrived the column was about to crash, but now it will not fall, for I am holding it up with all my strength. I shall only be able to return to you when not one heart on land or sea is suffering pain or sorrow."

Nicola was widely known and greatly beloved. Everyone mourned him but no one as much as the grieving princess. She never forgot the brave fisherman's son and spent her entire life trying to make the world a better place to live in so that he might return to her sooner.

THE TWINS OF
THE GOD MARS

* * * * * * * * * *

* * * * * * * * * *

THE proud and ancient city of Rome owes its name to a quarrel between two pagan brothers, one luckier than the other. For many centuries the story of Romolo and Remo, the founders of Rome, has been kept alive by Italian parents, who have told it and retold it to their children. Statues of the she-wolf who nursed the famous twins may be seen in many places in Rome. The Lupercal Cave and the site of the wolf's den on Palatine Hill are often pointed out, and in the steep, rocky wall of the Capitoline Hill occasionally stands a cage with a wolf inside to remind Roman children of the good mother-wolf.

Once long ago Numitore reigned as king of Alba, a small city set among green hills. He was a good and just ruler, but his brother, Prince Amulio, was an ambitious and wicked man, who waged every trick to rob Numitore of his power and fortune. He especially coveted the royal title. Only the king's two young children, a boy and a girl, stood in his way, so Amulio set about to remove them. He took his ten-year-old nephew out on dangerous hunting trips and on one of these the lad lost his life. He persuaded his young niece, Princess Rhea Silvia, to take the vows of a vestal virgin in the temple of Vesta, Goddess of the Hearth. These maidens, who were chosen from the best families, wore lovely white robes and were treated almost like goddesses by the people, who knelt before them when they passed on the street. They were expected to take turns at keeping the temple fire burning night and day. However, they were required to give up all thoughts of a husband and a home of their own. A vestal virgin found guilty of breaking her vows was locked in a cell and left there to die.

In those long-ago times, fire was a most precious possession. Sparks were struck only with difficulty by rubbing together two flints, stones or hard pieces of wood. The temple fire was even more difficult to light. It had to come directly from the sun through a small copper funnel, which was used only for that purpose. The guardians kept the funnel shining like gold so that it reflected the sun's rays as in a mirror. The concentrated heat caused the wood to burst into a bright flame that consumed the temple offerings of oil and incense. This temple fire was considered a sacred and divine gift from the gods. If the virgins let it go out or broke their vows, the people believed that Vesta would send down calamities to punish them.

For some time Princess Rhea Silvia was content as a vestal virgin. Then one lovely spring morning she went to the woods for water from the sacred fountain and met there a handsome young warrior. He knelt at her passing, as was the custom. They looked long in each other's eyes, and for the first time the beautiful Silvia felt the flame of love quicken in her heart. Yet when the youth spoke words of love to her, she begged him to be silent. "I am a vestal virgin," she said sadly, "and must not break my vows."

No mortal vows could stop him, the youth said, for he was none other than the God Mars. He continued to tell her of his love, and she at last returned it. They were married in secret and in due time Silvia gave birth to Romolo and Remo.

Her wily uncle, Prince Amulio, promised his niece that he would care for the children and arranged for Silvia to entrust her babies to him before she went to her death cell. Sadly she dressed them in their best and put them in a strong wicker basket. Her uncle turned them over to a trusted old hunter, saying, "Here, take them to the wild beasts in the woods and make certain they are no longer alive when you return here."

In the past the old hunter had always carried out Prince Amulio's orders without question, but he had not the heart to let the wolves tear the two innocent sleeping babes to pieces as his master had commanded. So, hoping that somehow they might be saved, he took the basket down to the Tiber where the river current would carry it away.

Since the twins were under the protection of their father, the God Mars, the Tiber treated them most gently. Instead of carrying the basket off into the wilderness, it floated it down only a short distance and let it become enmeshed in the roots of a fig tree at the mouth of the Lupercal Cave.

From there a motherly old wolf took the basket up to her den on what is now Rome's Palatine Hill, where she nursed the twins and let them play with her own cubs. A kindly woodpecker brought them food.

A short distance down the hill from the wolf's den stood the cabin where the shepherd Faustolo lived with his wife, Acca Lauranzia. They noticed the wolf's strangely gentle behavior and the woodpecker hovering over her den and, upon investigating, discovered the twins. Being childless, they took the babies home in secret and brought them up as their own.

As they grew older they easily became the leaders in games with their companions. The shepherd and his wife were proud of them. But though they loved Faustolo and Acca dearly, the boys never believed that they were their true parents.

As children, Romolo and Remo began taking part in the yearly festival in honor of Faunus, the god of shepherds and farmers. On one fateful February 15th, they were already tall and handsome youths in their early teens, and as they appeared in their goatskin coats, the people made way for them in admiration.

The ceremonies always took place in the Lupercal Grotto, which had been dedicated to Faunus. The priests chanted prayers and cut the throats of a goat and a mastiff, offering them as a sacrifice to the god. Afterward their skins were cut into strips and given to the younger priests and the strongest youths, who went about swinging them freely. It was considered good luck to be slapped by those skins.

Romolo and Remo were enjoying the melee when suddenly they heard cries for help. They found some of their friends being robbed of their best animals by some of King Numitore's insolent shepherds. A battle followed and hard blows were exchanged. The twins were able to get the animals back, but the shepherds swore vengeance on them.

Their opportunity for revenge came soon, when they came upon Remo alone in the woods with only a few companions. Remo and his friends put up a good fight, but they were overcome. The shepherds took Remo as a prisoner to the king. They accused him of nothing less than murder and wanted him punished. King Numitore, who had never seen his daughter's children, was impressed with the youth and his proud bearing. Surely, he said, this was no mere shepherd. He wanted to question Remo in private, so he sent his accusers away, promising them that justice would be done. Prince Amulio was taken aback by the presence of this handsome youth in the court and recognized him instantly as one of his nephews. He knew he must kill him before Numitore discovered his real identity and therefore urged that the youth be put to death.

In the meantime, Romolo heard that his brother was a prisoner in the king's palace and that Prince Amulio wanted him killed. So he lost no time in gathering a group of friends to go to his rescue. On the way to the palace, they were joined by many men who hated the evil prince and wished to be free of his tyranny. Romolo led a surprise attack on

Prince Amulio and he was killed, without one person to defend him.

The shepherd Faustolo now took the basket in which he had found the twins along with their baby clothes to King Numitore, for the time had come in which the mystery concerning them should be unraveled. Thus the king discovered to his great joy that Romolo and Remo were his own grandchildren, the sons of his beloved Rhea Silvia.

King Numitore immediately accorded his grandsons their proper royal rank. He offered to share his throne with Romolo and Remo. But they were accustomed to a free and independent life and wanted a kingdom of their own. As their grandfather wished only to please them, he gave his consent.

Then the question arose as to a proper site for a new city and as to who would rule where it was established. Remo favored what is now Aventine Hill and Romolo wanted to locate the city on what is now the Palatine. Each one claimed advantages for his choice. But as they could come to no agreement, they decided to leave the decision to the gods. They were to watch the heavens until sunset and the one who would see the greatest number of vultures pass over his chosen site would be considered the chosen one. Friends accompanied each brother and as the vultures passed, they called out the numbers. When the sun was almost sunk in the west, Remo's side called out, "Nine!" and Romolo's "Eight!" But immediately Romolo shouted, "Nine, ten, eleven, twelve. I win!"

Arguments arose as to whether Romolo saw the additional vultures before or after the sun had set. But the jubilant Romolo did not even listen. He lost no time in harnessing an ox and a heifer to a plow and traced a furrow around the Palatine Hill. Then he declared that this was the site for the city he would build and rule. "If anyone dares to cross this line," he warned, "he shall pay with his life!"

Remo became furious as he realized that his opportunity to rule was slipping away from him. He defied his brother and jumped over the furrow.

Romolo lost his head and in a great rage he cried out to the terrified shepherds around them, "Beware! I meant what I said!" And even as he spoke he drew his sword and killed his brother.

The new city was called "Roma," meaning "river" in Etruscan because it was on the Tiber and because it was part of the victorious Romolo's name. In order to attract settlers to it, King Romolo issued a proclamation that all who came to live in Rome would be free from slavery, debt and prison sentences. The city soon became populated but mostly by men. They worked hard to make it prosperous and beautiful, but there were no women for them to marry. The small kingdoms surrounding Rome would not trust their women to the Romans. Thus King Romolo sent out his youngest and strongest men to steal wives for themselves. The Romans married the women and treated them well, but their families demanded revenge and several wars were fought. But with the Sabines, however, King Romolo made peace and ruled along with the strong Sabine General Tazio.

During the first troubled years, King Romolo's rule was just and wise. But after the death of General Tazio, Romolo grew increasingly arrogant and tyrannical like his uncle Amulio. Although the common people were blind to his faults and continued to adore him, the Patricians, the upper classes, started to organize a revolt against King Romolo.

But Romolo's lucky star was still with him. Before any harm could come to him from his enemies, his father Mars swept down upon the earth during a violent summer storm, and bore Romolo away to the heavens. He was never seen again in Rome, but was worshipped ever after as the God Quirinus.

THE PRINCE OF THE
DOLOMITES AND THE
PRINCESS OF THE MOON

* * * * * * * * * *

* * * * * * * * * *

HE most beautiful mountains in Italy—perhaps in the whole world—are the Dolomites, a southeastern range of the Alps. Extraordinary in color and molded into many strange shapes by sun, wind and rain, some of the white limestone slopes resemble pyramids, some resemble walled towns with towering castles. Even when there is no snow on them their summits are white, and here and there a peak looks as if it were made of rosy alabaster. But they were not *always* white. . . .

Long, long ago a good king ruled over the Dolomites. His subjects, farmers and shepherds for the most part, lived in peace and contentment. Strangely enough, the one unhappy person among them was the king's only son. Handsome, brave, beloved by everyone and heir to his father's throne and fortune, the young prince had every reason to be happy. But he was obsessed by a longing to go to the moon and he brooded over it until he almost became ill. His friends tried to interest him in various amusements, but he would listen to no one.

The king, who was extremely concerned about his son, consulted the wise men of his own and neighboring king-

179

doms, but they all said a trip to the moon was impossible. In fact, behind his back they even made fun of the prince for his wild and impractical notions. But those old men, who were considered wise, were the foolish ones, for they did not know that with love everything is possible, even a trip to the moon.

One day the prince went hunting, but as usual, he was dreaming of the moon, and before he realized it, he had dismounted and wandered away from his party. He walked all afternoon, thinking he was going homeward, but when night fell, he found himself far from his father's castle on an unfamiliar plain with high rocky walls on three sides. Rhododendrons were growing beside the walls, and the ground was carpeted with grass. Wearily he flung himself down and immediately fell asleep.

He dreamed he was standing in a meadow covered with strange white flowers, holding a bouquet of rhododendrons in his hand. A beautiful girl whom he had never seen came toward him, and he immediately proffered to her his rhododendrons. She accepted them happily and asked where he and the beautiful flowers had come from. Then she introduced herself and the prince knew that at last his dearest wish had come true, for the lovely girl who stood before him was the daughter of the king of the moon.

The prince was overcome with joy, but before he could tell his charming companion of his lifelong dream, she had vanished and he was wide-awake. He rubbed his eyes sleepily and looked about him. The moon was high in the heavens, flooding the plain with its silver light, and as the prince remembered his dream, his desire to go to the moon and meet again the beautiful princess became almost unbearable.

Still in a daze, he arose from the ground and without realizing what he was doing, began to pick a bouquet of rhododendrons.

Suddenly, although there was no one except himself on the plain, the prince began hearing voices, and they seemed to come from one of the cloud-topped cliffs. "Can it be the spirits of the mountain?" he wondered. He felt for his sword and began making his way up the cliff.

The higher he climbed, the more distinct the voices became. But when he entered the cloud it was so dark that he had to grope his way until he struck against something hard. Then a door opened, and he found himself in a brightly lighted room in which two old men were seated. At the sight of the stranger both jumped up in fright. But the prince introduced himself and soon reassured them of his friendliness. Then the older of the two told him, "We are inhabitants of the moon and have just taken a long journey on earth. Now we are returning home."

The prince was not surprised when he heard he was in the presence of men from the moon, and he told them of his long-cherished wish to visit their country.

"Your wish can be fulfilled quite easily," they told him. "If you want to come with us, we can set out at once."

The prince was so overjoyed by the invitation that he could scarcely find words to express his gratitude. A moment later the cloud detached itself from the rock and began to fly lightly and swiftly toward the moon, carrying with it the three passengers. During the journey the prince told the old men about his father's kingdom, and they in turn described their country to him. However, one of them warned the prince that an earth-dweller could not remain long on the moon without becoming blind. "Mountains, plains, woods, lakes, rivers and cities shine like silver," the older one said, "and eyes not accustomed from birth to so much light could not bear the dazzling whiteness."

"Nor could a moon-dweller stay long in your country," the younger one added, "for it is too dark down there, and he would soon become ill."

When the three landed on the moon, the two old men showed the prince the way to their capital and, taking leave of him, went off in another direction. The prince had to go the rest of the way on foot, and as he walked on in this new, white world, it looked to him very much like the one he had seen in his dream, with the same white flowers covering the meadows. But here a clear white light emanated even from the sun.

When the prince reached the royal palace, he was surprised to find no guards, only a shining fence with a lovely flower garden beside it. A gardener approached, but before the prince could explain his visit to him, he spoke admiringly of the bouquet of flowers in his hand. "Our princess loves rare and beautiful flowers," the gardener said, "and if you will give these to her, she will reward you handsomely."

The prince smiled. "I shall be happy to give this bouquet to your princess, but I have no need of reward, for I am the son of the king of the Dolomites."

The gardener was obviously impressed by the importance of the visitor, for he opened the gate at once and then hurried ahead to announce him to the king. Soon he returned and invited the prince to follow him into the palace. They walked through many spacious rooms with alabaster walls and at last reached a great hall full of light. Here the king and his daughter, the princess of the moon, were waiting to receive him. The king looked very old and had a long white beard, but the princess, much to the surprise of the prince, was the same beautiful maiden he had seen in his dream.

Both father and daughter welcomed the visitor cordially and the princess accepted the bouquet of rhododendrons with delight. "Are all the flowers on earth as beautiful as these?" she asked, and he proceeded to tell her of the many lovely blossoms that grew in his land. After they had chatted pleasantly for a while, the king invited the prince to be their guest for as long as he wished to stay. The young man needed no urging, especially when he looked at the princess, who nodded smilingly.

From then on the prince of the Dolomites and the princess of the moon were constantly together. Often the prince thought to himself that he had indeed realized his dearest wish.

But after several weeks had passed, the prince, though still charmed by the princess and by her beautiful country, began to feel that all was not well. He had a strange burning sensation in his eyes, and often found himself closing them to shut out the dazzling light. His joy at being on the moon with the beautiful girl he loved and who loved him in return began to turn to pain. For he recalled what the old man had told him on their journey from the earth—that the moon was too luminous for the people of the earth and the earth too dark for the people of the moon.

One day at the dinner table, the old king asked him, "Well, my young friend, how do you like our country?"

"Your Majesty," he answered, "your country is the most beautiful I have ever seen, but I regret to say that its splendor is overwhelming. I fear that if I do not return soon to the earth, I shall become blind."

He had never expressed his fear to the princess, for he did not wish to alarm her, but she heard him speaking to her father and said quickly, "Oh, surely the longer you stay the more accustomed you will become to our white brilliance until perhaps one day it will not bother you at all."

Time passed quickly enough for the two young lovers on the moon, but not for the prince's unhappy father and people on earth, who believed him lost forever. When the prince failed to return to his hunting companions, they had searched for him for several days and nights until at last there was nothing left but to report his disappearance to the king, who drove them away in a fury and told them never to appear in his presence again if they could not bring back his son. In the following weeks and months the king sent out more search parties and issued a proclamation offering a handsome reward for news of the prince.

Hope for his return was growing dim when one day the startling news was heralded that the prince had at last returned to earth with a beautiful wife, none other than the daughter of the king of the moon. The prince had long desired to present his beloved wife to his father, so they had descended in the cloud chamber for a visit.

Everyone was happy, for the prince was well beloved, and his return was celebrated with splendid feasts, music and dancing.

The people found the princess of the moon exceedingly beautiful and observed that wherever she went she was bathed in a dazzling white radiance; if she walked under a tree, its shadow disappeared.

All admired the small white flowers she had brought with her, which she told them covered the mountains and fields of the moon like a blanket of snow. They were planted with loving care and with the passing of the years, began to flourish in the Dolomites. They grow there still and are called alpine stars, although they are better known by their German name, "edelweiss."

The princess, for her part, never tired of looking at the smiling fields of flowers of many colors, the green pastures, and the tiny blue-green, gemlike lakes of the Dolomites. She declared she much preferred the varied colors of the earth to the silver-white monotony of the moon. The prince was happy that his wife took such delight in his country, and he took pleasure in showing her all the beautiful places in his kingdom. Thus both were content and looked forward to a tranquil future.

But this happy state of affairs was soon to come to an end. Returning late one night from hunting, the prince saw his wife standing at an upper window, looking longingly at the moon. She seemed in a trance, oblivious to everything about her, and did not hear the prince enter the room. He noticed how pale she was and, thus taken by surprise, she confessed that for some time she had been ill with longing to return to her own land. "The mountains here are beautiful," she told him, "but their dark, gloomy peaks rise toward the sky like threatening giants and strike fear into my heart."

The prince reassured her and did everything to amuse his wife and to keep her from longing for the moon, but all his efforts were in vain, as those of his friends had been when he had pined to go there. She grew weaker daily; the doctors feared for her life but could do nothing to help her.

When the king of the moon heard of his daughter's condition, he came down to earth and declared he would not
stand by and let his daughter die of nostalgia. He prepared
to take his daughter back with him that very day and told
the prince he could do as he pleased about accompanying
them.

The prince decided to go with his wife and would not
listen to the pleas of his father nor to those of his people,
who begged him, for the good of the kingdom, not to leave
them again.

As soon as they returned to the moon the princess' health
began to improve, and within a short time she was her old
gay self again. But the poor prince began to lose his sight.
Each day he saw a little less until at last he became seriously
alarmed. The doctors advised him to return to earth at once,
or he would become blind. He did not want to leave his
wife, but finally yielded.

The moment he returned to his own land, his sight began
to improve, but all joy in life was ended for him. His passion
for the moon was stronger than ever, now that his wife was
there, and it gave him no peace. He could take no interest
in the affairs of the kingdom but would wander off into the
mountains to live alone. In time he did not return to the
palace at all but spent his days and nights in wandering
without finding any peace.

One day a terrific storm forced him to enter a cave for
shelter. Much to his surprise, he found himself in the presence of a curious little man, about three feet tall, with a sad
face, partly covered by a long beard, who wore on his head
a golden crown. He told the prince that he was the king of
the Salvani, dwarfs who inhabited caves and groves.

During the night, upon the prince's request, the sad little king told him his story. His people, he said, were once as numerous as the leaves on the trees and lived in their own strong kingdom in the eastern Alps. There they had lived in peace until their lands were invaded by a powerful, warlike people; only he and a few survivors escaped. He had sought a place of refuge for them in several neighboring kingdoms. All the Salvani wanted was one forest, one marsh, one piece of land where they could live in peace, but no one one would give it to them. Finally one king had given them permission to settle, but treated the little king and his little band of followers so badly that they could stand it no longer. At last they had scattered to the mountain-top where the prince had come upon their king.

The poor little king-without-a-kingdom sighed heavily as he finished his tale of woe, and said to the prince, "Now it is your turn to tell your story. Why are you here so far away from home in a place that no one ever visits?"

The prince, after not having talked with anyone for such a long time, was only too willing to tell his troubles to a sympathetic listener. But imagine his astonishment when he had finished to see the little king jump and shout, "We are all saved! We are all saved!"

The dwarf explained his idea quickly. "Your wife had to return to the moon because she was unable to bear the gloom of the dark mountain peaks. If they were white, she could live down here happily with you, isn't that so? Well, we Salvani, although small of stature, are clever. We can make as many mountains white as you wish, provided your father will permit us to live peacefully in his kingdom forever. What do you think of this?"

"Wonderful, if it were possible," replied the prince, a little incredulous. "It would not be difficult for me to obtain my father's assent to what you wish. But how will you make those mountains white?"

The dwarf smiled and said, "Oh, leave it to us. We have done more difficult things than that."

The prince, willing to take any step that might restore his happiness, suggested that they set out at once to see his father. The storm had ceased, but it took them two days to reach his castle. The king was overjoyed to see his son again. At first, however, he was uncertain about granting what he and the little king of the Salvani wanted. But when the dwarf king promised that they would never descend into the valleys and that they would never claim the fields or pastures, a treaty was concluded and both sides swore to observe the provisions. Then the happy little king set out to gather his scattered subjects to impart the good news and to set them to work.

A few days later the little men were seen filing along the mountain peaks bordering the kingdom. After they had found shelter in the ravines, in caves behind waterfalls and high in the mountains, their king sent word to the prince that the Salvani would start their work that very night.

The prince, torn between doubt and hope, had been anxiously awaiting the moment for them to begin. He climbed a peak and waited to see what would happen.

Scarcely had the moon come out when seven Salvani came out on the mountain where the prince was. They formed a circle and began to make strange movements in every direction, as though they were taking hold of something invisible. Their little hands moved and crossed one another in the air like birds. The prince observed their movements in wonder and asked what they were doing; they answered, "We are weaving with the light of the moon."

After a while a small, even, luminous skein of light began to form. The dwarfs continued working and as the hours passed, the skein grew and grew until it became a coverlet Looking all about him, the prince saw that the light illuminated every mountain top throughout the kingdom. It seemed as if all the stars of the heavens were descending upon every gloomy peak. The valleys were still full of shadows, as the moon illuminated only the highest points. But when its light disappeared completely, the little men began the second part of their task, that of unwinding large skeins of light and drawing long shining lines down the mountainsides. Then they circled the mountains, enveloping them all in a network of light and drawing threads in and out until the last dark spots disappeared and all was luminously white.

The next morning the inhabitants of the Dolomites beheld a strange sight; they thought surely their eyes were deceiving them. The slopes of the mountains, which had been bleak and forbidding the day before, were now white and festive, in vivid contrast to the deep green of pines and firs. In one night the little Salvani had been able to deck all the mountains of the kingdom with the clear light of the moon.

When the prince, radiant with joy, returned to the castle the next morning, he found a messenger from the moon awaiting him with the sad news that his wife was dying of a strange malady and had expressed a wish to see him once more. He hurried up to the moon and, kneeling by her bedside, he pleaded. "You must not die now, my beloved, for henceforth we need never be separated. You can come down

with me to earth, which I have had made white for you with the light from the moon. The mountaintops are no longer dark, but burn amidst the clouds like silver flames. You need never again pine for your country. Now you must get well so that we may live happily together."

Again love worked its miracle. The baffling illness which the doctors had been unable to halt came from being separated from the prince, whom she loved more than life itself. She began to improve at once, and within a short time he was able to take her home with him to a fair land in which white mountains, green flowering valleys and all the rich colors of the earth were mingled with the luminous light of the moon. There, at the foot of the white and rose-tinted Dolomites, the prince and his wife, united once more, lived happily together. And, in token of their gratitude, the little Salvani, whose handiwork had made their happiness possible, were treated with the greatest respect to the end of their days.